AF820760

Gynecologic and Obstetric Investigation

Founded 1895 as 'Monatsschrift für Geburtshilfe und Gynäkologie', continued 1946–1969 as 'Gynaecologia' and 1970–1977 as 'Gynecologic Investigation'

Founders: A. Martin and M. Sänger
Former Editors: E. Anderes (1939–1952), Th. Koller (1939–1969), O. Käser (1954–1969), R. Wenner (1959–1967), P. Bloch (1965–1969), W.L. Hermann (1970–1975), P.J. Keller (1976–1984), G. Zador (1985–2001)

KARGER

Printed in Switzerland on acid-free paper by Reinhardt Druck, Basel

Appears 6-weekly: 2 volumes per year (8 issues)

Guidelines for Authors

Gynecologic and Obstetric Investigation

Submission

Only original papers, carefully selected case reports, and invited reviews written in English are considered and should be sent to:

Editorial Office 'Gynecologic and Obstetric Investigation'
S. Karger AG
P.O. Box
CH–4009 Basel (Switzerland)
Tel. +41 61 306 1344
Fax +41 61 306 1434
E-Mail s.aeschbach@karger.ch

Mailing address for courier deliveries only:
Allschwilerstr. 10
CH–4055 Basel (Switzerland)

Manuscripts should be submitted in quadruplicate (with four sets of illustrations of which one is an original), typewritten double-spaced on one side of the paper, with a wide margin.

Conditions

All manuscripts are subject to editorial review. *Original Papers* should not exceed 4 printed pages (12 manuscript pages), including tables, illustrations and references. *Articles on current investigation* are limited to 2 printed pages (6 manuscript pages). *Case Reports* are carefully selected and limited to 2 printed pages (6 manuscript pages): this includes statements of the problem, patient history, diagnosis, treatment, results and any other information pertinent to the case and maximum 5 references. *Reviews* are usually commissioned; however, the Editor-in-Chief is happy to discuss potential articles with authors who would like to contribute. Submission of an article for publication implies the transfer of the copyright from the author to the publisher upon acceptance. Accepted papers become the permanent property of 'Gynecologic and Obstetric Investigation' and may not be reproduced by any means, in whole or in part, without the written consent of the publisher. It is the author's responsibility to obtain permission to reproduce illustrations, tables, etc. from other publications.

All manuscripts must be accompanied by a covering letter signed by all authors. Assurance should be given that the manuscript is not under simultaneous consideration by any other publication.

All manuscripts originating from non-English-speaking countries must be revised by a professional linguistic reviewer and it must be evident from the covering letter that this has been done.

Good clinical practice: It has become mandatory that every trial in humans must first obtain approval from an independent Ethics Committee and formal, informed consent from the patients before they participate in a clinical study or experiment. In order to avoid unnecessary delay with the review of manuscripts, authors are kindly asked to state, preferably in the Materials and Methods section, that approval and informed consent have been obtained. These two statements must also appear on the covering letter which accompanies every manuscript and is signed by each author.

Arrangement

All pages should be consecutively numbered beginning with the title page, then the text, acknowledgements, references and legends to figures. The text in original papers should be divided under the headings: Abstract, Introduction, Material(s) and Method(s), Results, and Discussion. The text in case reports should be divided under the headings: Introduction, Case Report(s) and Conclusion(s).

Title page: The first page of each paper should indicate the title, the authors' names, and the institute where the work was conducted. A short title for use as running head as well as the full address of the author to whom correspondence should be sent are also required.

Full address: The exact postal address complete with postal code must be given at the bottom of the title page. Please also supply phone and fax numbers, as well as your e-mail address.

Key words: For indexing purposes, a list of 3–10 key words in English is essential.

Abstract: The first page of the text should include an abstract of up to 10 lines.

Footnotes: Avoid footnotes. When essential, they are numbered consecutively and typed at the foot of the appropriate page.

Tables and illustrations: Tables and illustrations (both numbered in Arabic numerals) should be prepared on separate sheets. Tables require a heading and figures a legend, also prepared on a separate sheet. For the reproduction of illustrations, only good drawings and original photographs can be accepted; negatives or photocopies cannot be used. Due to technical reasons, figures with a screen background should not be submitted. When possible, group several illustrations on one block for reproduction (max. size 181 × 223 mm) or provide crop marks. On the back of each illustration, indicate its number, the author's name, and 'top' with a soft pencil.

Color illustrations: Up to 6 color illustrations per page can be integrated within the text at the reduced price of CHF 660.– / USD 545.00 per page. Color illustrations are reproduced at the author's expense.

References: In the text identify references by Arabic numerals [in square brackets]. Material submitted for publication but not yet accepted should be noted as 'unpublished data' and not be included in the reference list. The list of references should include only those publications which are cited in the text. Do not alphabetize; number references in the order in which they are first mentioned in the text. The surnames of the authors followed by initials should be given. There should be no punctuation other than a comma to separate the authors. Cite all authors, 'et al' is not sufficient. Abbreviate journal names according to the Index Medicus system. (Also see International Committee of Medical Journal Editors: Uniform requirements for manuscripts submitted to biomedical journals. N Engl J Med 1997;336:309–315.)

Examples

(a) Papers published in periodicals: Sun J, Koto H, Chung KF: Interaction of ozone and allergen challenges on bronchial responsiveness and inflammation in sensitised guinea pigs. Int Arch Allergy Immunol 1997;112:191–195.

(b) Monographs: Matthews DE, Farewell VT: Using and Understanding Medical Statistics, ed 3, revised. Basel, Karger, 1996.

(c) Edited books: Parren PWHI, Burton DR: Antibodies against HIV-1 from phage display libraries: Mapping of an immune response and progress towards antiviral immunotherapy; in Capra JD (ed): Antibody Engineering. Chem Immunol. Basel, Karger, 1997, vol 65, pp 18–56.

Page charges

There are no page charges for papers of 4 or fewer printed pages (including tables, illustrations and references). Each additional complete or partial page is charged to the author at CHF 275.– / USD 196.00. The allotted size of a paper is equal to approx. 12 manuscript pages (including tables, illustrations and references).

Galley proofs

Unless indicated otherwise, galley proofs are sent to the first-named author and should be returned with the least possible delay. Alterations made in galley proofs, other than the correction of printer's errors, are charged to the author. No page proofs are supplied.

Reprints

Order forms and a price list are sent with the galley proofs. Orders submitted after the issue is printed are subject to considerably higher prices.

KARGER

Fax + 41 61 306 12 34
E-Mail karger@karger.ch
www.karger.com

The Guidelines for Authors are available at:
www.karger.com/goi_Guidelines

General Information

Gynecologic and Obstetric Investigation

Publication data: 'Gynecologic and Obstetric Investigation' is published 8 times a year. Volumes 53–54 with 4 issues each appear in 2002.

Subscription rates: Subscriptions run for a full calendar year. Prices are given per volume.

Personal subscription:
Subscription + postage and handling
CHF 371.50 + CHF 19.20 Europe
CHF 371.50 + CHF 28.50 Overseas
USD 286.00 + USD 19.20
+ online subscription per volume:
CHF 39.– / USD 30.00
(Must be in the name of, billed to, and paid by an individual. Order must be marked 'personal subscription'.)

Institutional subscription:
Subscription + postage and handling
CHF 743.– + CHF 24.– Europe
CHF 743.– + CHF 35.60 Overseas
USD 572.00 + USD 24.00
+ online subscription per volume:
CHF 58.– / USD 45.00

Airmail postage: CHF 25.20, USD 21.00.
(Extra per volume.)

Discount subscription prices:
Society for Gynecologic Investigation

Microforms: Please direct all enquiries and orders to:
University Microfilms Inc.
300 North Zeeb Road, P.O. Box 1346
Ann Arbor, MI 48106-1346 (USA)

Subscription orders: Orders can be placed at agencies, bookstores, directly with the Publisher
S. Karger AG, P.O. Box,
CH–4009 Basel (Switzerland)
or with any of the following distributors:
Deutschland: S. Karger GmbH, Postfach
D–79095 Freiburg
France: Librairie Luginbühl
36, bd de Latour-Maubourg, F–75007 Paris
Great Britain, Ireland: S. Karger AG
4 Rickett Street
London SW6 1RU, UK
USA: S. Karger Publishers, Inc.
26 West Avon Road, P.O. Box 529
Farmington, CT 06085, USA
India, Bangladesh, Sri Lanka:
Panther Publishers Private Ltd.
33, First Main
Koramangala First Block
Bangalore 560 034, India
Japan: Karger Japan, Inc.
Yushima S Bld. 3F
4-2-3, Yushima, Bunkyo-ku
Tokyo 113-0034, Japan

Change of address: Both old and new address should be sent to the subscription source.

Single issues and back volumes: Information can be obtained through the Publisher.

Advertising: Correspondence and rate requests should be addressed to the Publisher.

Bibliographic indices: This journal is regularly listed in bibliographic services, including *Current Contents®*.

Book Reviews: Books are accepted for review by special agreement.

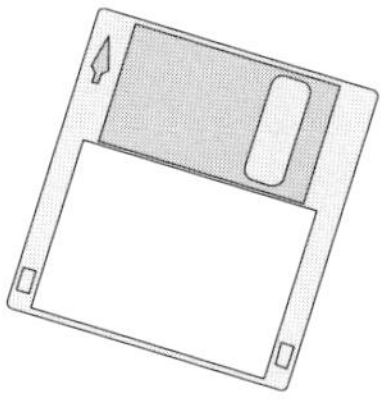

Disk Submission

A **comprehensive version** of these guidelines for the **submission of manuscripts and illustrations on disk** can be accessed online under **www.karger.com/disksubmission** or requested as a leaflet from the editorial department.

Please follow the general rules on style and arrangement in the **'Guidelines for Authors'** of the journal. Submit a **double-spaced printout** of your manuscript matching the file on disk exactly.

Technical Information
Store only data pertinent to this manuscript. Include your fonts (screen and printer fonts for Macintosh). For a **text only** manuscript, use a 3.5-inch disk. For **text and illustrations,** use 3.5 or 5.25 Magneto Optical Disc; CD-ROM (DOS or hybrid); iomega Zip/DOS (100 MB), or 44 MB, 88 MB or 200 MB SyQuest. Compress extensive data using ZIP format.

Data Description
Label your disk with the **title of the journal or book** for which it is submitted; a **short version** of the paper's title; your **name,** postal and e-mail address, fax and phone number; **hard- and software** used, including the version; and the **complete list of the file names.** File names consist of eight characters before the dot identifying the file and three characters after the dot identifying the application.

Text and Format
The **preferred word-processing package is MS-Word.** Other commonly used PC text programs and ASCII formats are accepted.
Update your data when you revise subsequent to the reviewer's or editor's decision and mark revisions clearly. Manuscripts accepted for publication are subject to **copy editing:** changes and/or questions will be marked in the manuscript, which will be returned to you with your disk and the galley proofs for checking.
Enter your text continuously flush left. Do not use any layout functions. Do not split words at the end of a line. **Do not use indentations.** Use a blank line before and a hard return at the end of paragraphs.
Arrange headings flush left. Insert only **one space after punctuation marks.** Insert Greek letters, mathematical symbols etc. with your word-processing program. Use **boldface and italics** as well as sub- and superscript where appropriate.
Tables are part of the text and should be placed at the end of the text file. Separate the individual parts of a table by lines. Use the tabulator instead of spaces. Format operation data on one line in the same column.

Legends to illustrations are part of the text and should also be listed at the end of the text file.

Illustrations
Store illustrations as separate files: do not integrate them in your text. Export **line drawings/vector graphics** as TIF, EPS or WMF format. Use Photoshop for processing and retouching **scanned halftone images.** Save the original scan and the processed version. Export **black and white or color images** as TIF or EPS format in their anticipated size in print.
For detailed information on how to submit illustration data on disk please consult the leaflet or **www.karger.com/disksubmission**

KI 02 DISK

KARGER

Fax +41 61 306 12 34
E-Mail karger@karger.ch
www.karger.com

The Journal Home Page is available at:
www.karger.com/goi

A Picture Book of Molecules!

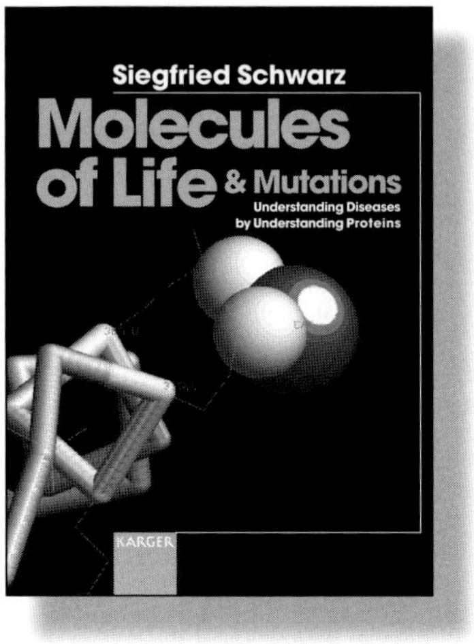

Siegfried Schwarz

Molecules of Life and Mutations

Understanding Diseases by Understanding Proteins

Molecular Biology; Biochemistry; General Medicine, Molecular Medicine, Pharmacology, Endocrinology

This book provides insights into the structures and functions of 130 of the most important biomolecules and their interactions with other endogenous or exogenous molecules. These interactions are illustrated by 3-dimensional images of their atomic structures rather than by abstract formulas or acronyms. The author has compiled an extraordinary collection of molecules which he has visualized by applying molecular modelling software to their atomic coordinate files (deposited in the Brookhaven Protein Data Bank, PDB). Together with short explanatory texts they provide the reader with a deepened understanding of biological phenomena in the normal as well as the diseased organism.
The book distills the most important facts in a clear and concise manner, and, at the same time, it serves as a guide to the vast amount of information stored in authoritative Internet databases such as the PDB and OMIM (Online Mendelian Inheritance in Men) databanks. An enhanced index listing databank accession numbers, gene name and chromosomal location of each molecule under consideration is added. A detailed list of useful Internet resources rounds off the practical value of this textbook.
Mutations can cause diseases by producing functionally altered proteins, and understanding the exact nature of diseases from the structures of the proteins involved is the aim of this book. Impressive both by its instructive and its esthetic quality, it reflects the newly emerging field of molecular medicine and thus will be appreciated not only by biologists, physicians and pharmacologists, but will also be especially useful to medical students and lecturers, and anyone with an interest in the life sciences.

KI 02277

Contents

www.karger.com/molecules_of_life

Schwarz, S. (Innsbruck)
Molecules of Life and Mutations
Understanding Diseases by Understanding Proteins
XIV + 144 p., 475 color fig., hard cover, 2002
CHF 88.– / EUR 63.00 / USD 76.50
Prices subject to change
EUR price for Germany, USD price for USA only
ISBN 3-8055-7395-2
Distributed in Japan exclusively by Igaku Shoin Ltd., Tokyo

KARGER

Order Form

Please send: ____ copy/ies

Postage and handling free with prepayment

Payment:
☐ Check enclosed ☐ Please bill me

Please charge to my credit card
☐ American Express ☐ Diners ☐ Eurocard
☐ MasterCard ☐ Visa

Card No.: __________

Exp. date: __________

Orders may be placed with any bookshop, subscription agency, directly with the publisher or through a Karger distributor.

Fax: +41 61 306 12 34
S. Karger AG, P.O. Box, CH–4009 Basel (Switzerland)
E-Mail karger@karger.ch, **www.karger.com**

Name/Address: __________

Date: __________

Signature: __________

Gynecologic and
Obstetric Investigation

The Fifth Japan Conference on Endometriosis

Management of Endometriosis

Proceedings of the Fifth Japan Conference on Endometriosis
Hakone Prince Hotel, Kanagawa, Japan, May 18, 2002

Guest Editors
H. Hoshiai, Osaka-Sayama
Y. Taketani, Tokyo
N. Terakawa, Yonago

18 figures and 13 tables, 2002

KARGER
Basel · Freiburg · Paris · London · New York ·
New Delhi · Bangkok · Singapore · Tokyo · Sydney

The current meeting and publication were made possible by an educational grant from Takeda Chemical Industries, Ltd.

Editorial development by BIOMEDIS International, Ltd.

S. Karger
Medical and Scientific Publishers
Basel · Freiburg · Paris · London
New York · New Delhi · Bangkok
Singapore · Tokyo · Sydney

Printed in Switzerland on acid-free paper by
Reinhardt Druck, Basel
ISBN 3–8055–7510–6

KARGER

Fax + 41 61 306 12 34
E-Mail karger@karger.ch
www.karger.com

Vol. 54, Suppl. 1, 2002

Gynecologic and Obstetric Investigation

Contents

KARGER

Fax + 41 61 306 12 34
E-Mail karger@karger.ch
www.karger.com

Access to full text and tables of contents, including tentative ones for forthcoming issues:
www.karger.com/goi_issues

Gynecologic and
Obstetric Investigation

Gynecol Obstet Invest 2002;54(suppl 1):1
DOI: 10.1159/000066286

Introduction

Hiroshi Hoshiai, Kinki University
Yuji Taketani, Tokyo University
Naoki Terakawa, Tottori University

This supplement presents the informative lectures and discussions featured at the 5th Japan Conference on Endometriosis held in Hakone, Japan, on May 18, 2002. The topic of this year's conference, sponsored by Takeda Chemical Industries, Ltd., was the management of endometriosis. There are many unanswered questions regarding this common disease. In an effort to promote a better understanding of endometriosis, a panel of experts in the field reviewed leading research concerning etiology, diagnosis, and treatment.

Noting that medical therapy alone is relatively ineffective for the treatment of endometriosis-associated infertility and pelvic pain, Professor Jacques Donnez (Université Catholique de Louvain) reviewed the literature to determine whether combined laparoscopic surgery consisting of laser vaporization, coagulation, or excision combined with adjuvant medical therapy with gonadotropin-releasing hormone agonists would be more effective. In a second presentation, Professor Donnez summarized current thinking on the histogenesis of endometriosis. He reviewed the probable stages in the development of peritoneal endometriosis and the prevailing theories concerning the source of the cells responsible for the development of ovarian and rectovaginal endometriosis. This supplement also includes an article by Professor Donnez's colleague, Dr. Jean Squifflet, on the diagnosis and imaging of adenomyotic disease of the retroperitoneal space.

Uterosacral nerve ablation is useful for some patients with dysmenorrhea whose pain is not relieved by nonsteroidal anti-inflammatory drugs. Dr. Miho Fujii of Sapporo Medical University reports on her group's histological localization of the nerves associated with the pain of dysmenorrhea. They also investigated the optimal site and cutting depth for uterosacral nerve ablation.

Dr. Mikio Momoeda of the University of Tokyo studied the findings of a nation-wide, multicenter cross-sectional survey of over 1,000 women with endometriosis to discover whether pain was actually associated with this diagnosis, and if so, to determine any links between disease stage and type of pain.

Treatment of ovarian endometrioma remains a matter of some debate. Dr. Souichi Yoshida of Tottori University assessed the effects of laparoscopic surgery on the symptoms of this common lesion and evaluated whether serum levels of IL-6 can be useful as a clinical indicator in the management of endometrioma.

Dr. Naoyuki Takuma of Asahikawa Medical College evaluated the utility of laparoscopic surgery for the treatment of infertile women by retrospective review of diagnostic and surgical laparoscopic records from Asahikawa Medical College Hospital from 1989 to 1998. Dr. Takuma used these data to help define the optimal procedure for treatment of endometriosis, including ovarian endometrioma.

Endometriosis can present special problems for young women who require assisted reproductive technology. It is known that the presence of an ovarian endometrial cyst adversely affects oocyte quality. However, resection of the cyst reduces the ovarian reserve available for exogenous hormone stimulation, and can be an unacceptable alternative to young women wishing to conceive. Dr. Nobuhiko Suganuma of Toyohashi Municipal Hospital analyzed the outcomes of women undergoing in vitro fertilization with or without cystectomy or aspiration of the ovarian cyst to determine the optimal pretreatment for in vitro fertilization and embryo transfer.

Fortunately, there have been many breakthroughs in the treatment of the pain and infertility associated with endometriosis. Recent advances in surgical techniques have provided physicians with new methods for the management of this chronic condition. We invite the reader to share in the wealth of new information on endometriosis included in this supplement, and hope that this knowledge will extend the available therapeutic options for women with this common, painful disease.

KARGER

Fax + 41 61 306 12 34
E-Mail karger@karger.ch
www.karger.com

0378–7346/02/0545–0001$18.50/0

Accessible online at:
www.karger.com/goi

Session 1
Review

Gynecologic and Obstetric Investigation

Gynecol Obstet Invest 2002;54(suppl 1):2–10
DOI: 10.1159/000066288

The Efficacy of Medical and Surgical Treatment of Endometriosis-Associated Infertility and Pelvic Pain

Jacques Donnez Jean Squifflet Céline Pirard Pascale Jadoul Christine Wyns Mireille Smets

Department of Gynecology, Université Catholique de Louvain, Brussels, Belgium

Key Words
Infertility · Pelvic pain · Endometriosis · Ovarian endometriosis

Abstract
This article is a review of the efficacy of medical and surgical treatment of endometriosis-associated infertility and pelvic pain. Endometriosis is the cause of pelvic pain (dysmenorrhea, dyspareunia) and infertility in more than 35% of women of reproductive age. Complete resolution of endometriosis is not yet possible but therapy has essentially three main objectives: (1) to reduce pain; (2) to increase the possibility of pregnancy; (3) to delay recurrence for as long as possible. It could be concluded that a consensus will probably never be reached on minimal and mild endometriosis. Nevertheless, because the Canadian study reported a large number of cases, we strongly support the view that visible endometriosis must be removed at the time of surgery. In cases of moderate and severe endometriosis-associated infertility, the combined approach (operative laparoscopy with GnRH-a) must be considered as 'first-line' treatment. The mean pregnancy rate of 50% reported in the literature following surgery provides scientific proof that operative treatment should be undertaken first to give our patients the best chance of conceiving naturally.

Introduction

Recently, a debate was published discussing whether the combination of laparoscopic surgery by laser, coagulation or excision and adjuvant medical therapy with GnRH agonists (GnRH-a) was the most appropriate treatment for endometriosis [1].

Endometriosis-Associated Pelvic Pain

Although laparoscopy is commonly used for the diagnosis and treatment of women with endometriosis and pelvic pain, Winkel [2] suggested, in a recent review, that surgical therapy offers no better results in terms of pain relief than medical therapy with GnRH-a [3]. Long-acting agonist treatment with addback therapy is another option that should also be considered among the armamentarium of therapy for patients with extensive and severe endometriosis.

To illustrate that results after purely surgical therapy of endometriosis are not satisfactory, we propose data from Wheeler's report [4]. Four hundred and twenty patients were followed up and cumulative 3- and 5-year recurrence rates of 13.5% and 40.3%, respectively, were obtained. The severity of the disease was not predictive of recurrence. Bearing this in mind, the better results achieved

KARGER
Fax + 41 61 306 12 34
E-Mail karger@karger.ch
www.karger.com

0378–7346/02/0545–0002$18.50/0

Accessible online at:
www.karger.com/goi

Jacques Donnez, MD, PhD
Department of Gynecology, Catholic University of Louvain
Cliniques Universitaires St-Luc
Avenue Hippocrate 10, B–1200, Brussels (Belgium)
Tel. +32 2 764 9502, Fax +32 2 764 9507, E-Mail donnez@gyne.ucl.ac.be

after GnRH-a administration and surgery look promising.

According to Telimaa et al. [5], patients who were medically treated had significantly less pelvic pain and smaller peritoneal implants at second-look laparoscopy. Therefore, postoperative medical treatment, causing hypoestrogenism and amenorrhea, might delay the recurrence of endometriotic symptoms [6]. Patients treated with nafarelin after laparoscopic surgery suffered less pain and had a longer pain-free interval than control subjects [7].

The results of endometriosis therapy with GnRH-a alone are very disappointing. Following laparoscopic diagnosis of endometriosis in 130 patients, Waller and Shaw [8] administered GnRH-a treatment for 6 months. Most of the women underwent second-look laparoscopy. The cumulative recurrence rate for the fifth year after cessation of treatment was 53.4% (36.9% for minimal disease and 74% for severe disease). The authors concluded that patients treated with GnRH-a alone stand a greater chance of suffering a recurrence, particularly if the disease is more severe. A second trial confirmed the poor results of purely medical therapy. Miller et al. [6] retrospectively analyzed data from 327 patients treated for 6 months with danazol (128/327) or GnRH-a (199/327). The mean interval before pain recurrence was 6.1 months in the danazol group and 5.2 in the GnRH-a group. Recurrence times varied with the stage of endometriosis. Miller et al. [6] found this rapid recurrence of pain disappointing in both treatment groups.

In our group, we clearly demonstrated that relatively hormone-independent endometriotic lesions persisted after GnRH-a treatment [9, 10].

Medical Therapy Alone Is Not Efficacious

Some arguments support the view that medical therapy alone is relatively inefficacious. Indeed, histology has proven the persistence of endometriotic implants after GnRH-a administration [9] and the persistence of residual activity (high mitotic index and KI 67) in hormone-independent residual foci with low steroid levels [11].

Moreover, ectopic endometrium (like normal endometrium) is capable of proliferating under the influence of estrogens even after a long time without estrogens [10]. The adhesion score has been clearly shown to be unchanged after GnRH-a [9, 12, 13].

Moreover, the rectovaginal adenomyotic nodule, considered as a distinct entity, requires a surgical approach because of the poor response to any medical therapy [14, 15].

Endometriosis-Associated Infertility

The first concept we should bear in mind is that peritoneal, ovarian, and rectovaginal endometriotic lesions must be considered as three different entities [10, 16]. The second is to differentiate patients with minimal or mild endometriosis from those with moderate or severe endometriosis. The third is to differentiate patients with endometriosis-associated pelvic pain from those with endometriosis-associated infertility.

Minimal and Mild Endometriosis-Associated Infertility

In infertile women presenting with minimal or mild endometriosis (American Fertility Society, or AFS classification), laparoscopic 'destruction' was proven to be the first line of therapy [17], but the recently published Italian study [18] demonstrated exactly the opposite. It is very curious that two evidence-based medicine (EBM) (degree 1) studies on the same subject reached two completely different conclusions.

In the first study [17], 341 infertile women (20–39 years of age) with minimal or mild endometriosis were randomized into two groups: either laparoscopic resection or ablation of the endometriotic lesions (n = 172), or diagnostic laparoscopy (n = 165). Cumulative pregnancy rates of 30.7 and 17.7%, respectively, were achieved. The authors concluded that laparoscopic resection or ablation of minimal and mild endometriosis enhances fecundity in infertile women. The most frequently cited bias is that patients were aware of the randomization. Another possible bias could be that mapping of the lesions was not considered in the selection at the time. Moreover, no distinction was made between red, black, and white lesions. The vascularization and mitotic activity, which are criteria suspected of inducing infertility, were not taken into account. This surely influenced the peritoneal fluid content and the peritoneal inflammatory reaction with, as a consequence, cytokine production and macrophage induction [19].

The results of the study published by the 'Gruppo Italiano per lo studio dell'endometriosis' [18] do not support the hypothesis that ablation of endometriotic lesions markedly improves fertility rates. Here too, bias exists:

firstly, the series is small (54 versus 47 patients); secondly, seven centers participated in the study, giving a mean of 14 patients per center; thirdly, histological confirmation of the diagnosis of endometriosis was not requested; and lastly, the percentage of active red lesions or non-active black or fibrotic lesions was not given. There was also no information on the vascularization and mitotic activity of the lesions. It is easy to criticize, but which study should we believe if we agree that both studies are supposed to be randomized controlled trials? We are therefore faced with the following question: do we really need evidence-based medicine (degree I) when we know that two prospective, randomized controlled studies have led to two completely opposing conclusions?

We can conclude that, because of the limited information currently available on the activity of lesions described in studies on mild or minimal endometriosis, any absolute statement on endometriosis and infertility is probably inappropriate at this time. Nevertheless, it seems that there are more arguments in favor of treating minimal and mild endometriosis at laparoscopy, if laparoscopy is decided upon.

Moderate and Severe Endometriosis-Associated Infertility

Consensus can be more easily established in the management of moderate and severe endometriosis. Indeed, in moderate and severe endometriosis, most patients present with ovarian endometriosis and/or periadnexal adhesions. Medical therapy alone is not effective in reducing endometriotic cysts and adhesions [13].

Do we really need evidence-based medicine to prove that ovarian chocolate cysts must be removed? Do we really need prospective, randomized studies to prove that a nodule more than 3 cm in size in the rectovaginal space must be removed? Do we really need to carry out this type of investigation, since we know that in rectovaginal nodules, there is a close histological relationship between nerves and endometriotic foci and fibrotic components of the nodules [20] and that lateral extension of rectovaginal nodules can provoke silent kidney damage in 10% of cases [16, 21]?

Is it not too easy to say: 'no EBM, no proof' and then to claim the contrary? All too frequently, papers published in the late 1980s are not mentioned because some gynecologists simply prefer to access Med-line. We cannot forget that a progressive disease like endometriosis can affect women as young as 15–16 years of age. Nobody is born with stage 4 endometriosis. But if we favor expectant management for stage 4 disease, then we will probably soon be obliged to add stage 5, 6, etc. to the present classification. We have always proposed combined therapy with surgery and GnRH-a.

In the late 1980s, we initiated a combined treatment with hormonal therapy followed by surgery [22]. Pregnancy rates of more than 52% were achieved in moderate endometriosis and more than 45% in severe endometriosis.

In a study published in 1996 [23], in 814 women presenting with ovarian endometriomas, we observed a cumulative pregnancy rate of 51% after combined treatment with GnRH-a and laparoscopic surgery. The majority of pregnancies occurred within 10 months of surgery (fig. 1).

Drainage alone of chocolate cysts is ineffective and only subsequent GnRH-a administration can reduce endometrioma size, periovarian inflammation and glandular mitotic activity [13]. Another obvious benefit is that absence of corpus luteum and/or follicles makes ovarian surgery easier. We therefore propose surgically removing the residual endometriosis after medical therapy.

We recently published a different hypothesis on the development of ovarian endometriosis [23, 24]. Celomic metaplasia of invaginated epithelial inclusions could be responsible for this pathogenesis. This hypothesis, based on the metaplastic potential of the pelvic mesothelium, is already a widely accepted theory on the pathogenesis of common epithelial ovarian tumors [25].

We believe that ovarian endometriosis is caused by metaplasia of invaginated celomic epithelium [23]. Our arguments are as follows:

(1) In our series, we found that 12% of endometriomas were not fixed to the broad ligament.

(2) It was not unusual to find multilocular endometriomas that could not be explained by the adhesion theory.

(3) The epithelium covering the ovary, which is the mesothelium, can invaginate into the ovarian cortex. Invaginations of the mesothelial layer covering the ovarian tissue were described by Motta et al. [26]. In our serial sections of the ovary, we frequently observed mesothelial inclusions.

(4) The fact that primordial follicles were found surrounding the endometriotic cyst is also in agreement with our hypothesis.

(5) Our main argument is based upon the presence of epithelial invaginations in continuum with endometrial tissue, proving the metaplasia theory [23, 27, 28].

(6) Endometriomas have been described in patients with Rokitansky-Küster-Hauser syndrome, who do not have a uterus, and therefore do not have retrograde menstruation [29].

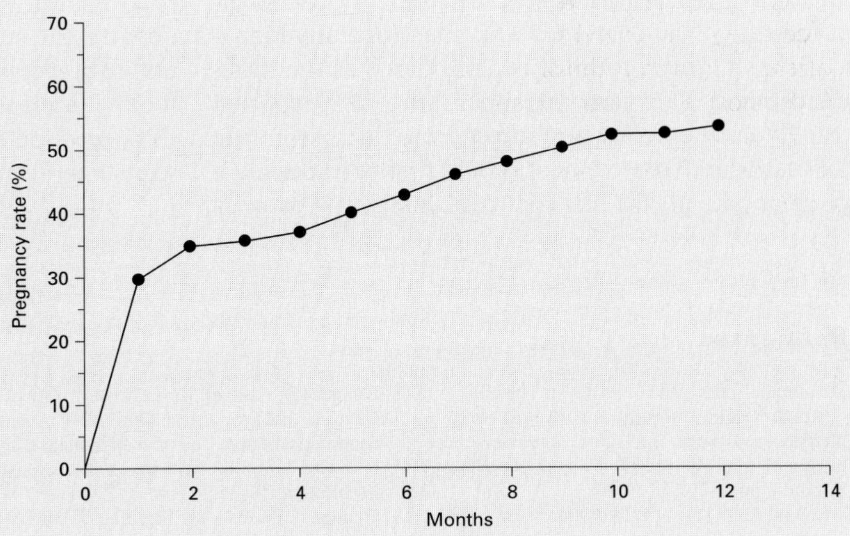

Fig. 1. Pregnancy rate during the first year after surgery. Adapted with permission from Donnez J, et al. [23].

(6) Common epithelial tumors of the ovary are considered to be derived from the surface epithelium covering the ovary and from the underlying stroma [25]. Why not the endometrioma?

These findings give us further arguments in favor of the surgical technique already proposed in 1987, which consists of vaporization of the internal wall of the cyst [30]. The depth of vaporization is shallow; only the glandular epithelium and the subjacent stroma have to be vaporized. There is no need to destroy the fibrotic capsule usually found surrounding the endometrioma. This technique avoids the removal of oocytes, frequently observed when the endometriotic capsule is removed during ovarian cystectomy. Brosens et al. [31] also confirmed that ovarian cystectomy was not mandatory for the management of large endometriomas. Their study and our own strongly suggest that it is only necessary to destroy the internal lining of the endometrioma, histologically represented by glandular epithelium, endometrial glands, and stroma, to minimize ovarian trauma and avoid the risk of premature ovarian failure. Performing the procedure after GnRH-a therapy is easier because of the reduced thickness of the endometrial wall.

Audebert et al. [32] showed that, in the case of combined medico-surgical treatment for stage III–IV endometriosis, preoperative medical therapy with GnRH-a gives a greater improvement in the AFS score. Indeed, AFS scores were found to be significantly better when nafarelin was given prior to surgery. However, the authors confirmed that no conclusion could be reached if preoperative treatment facilitates surgery. In a recent review, Johnson [33] concluded that all symptomatic endometriotic diseases should be treated early and aggressively. After conservative surgical resection of all apparent endometriosis, he strongly advocates medical treatment with GnRH-a. Some authors [7, 34] have concluded that adjuvant GnRH-a therapy after laparoscopic surgery for endometriosis significantly delays the return of endometriosis symptoms requiring further treatment, and confirmed our hypothesis that combined GnRH-a and operative treatment for endometriosis is the best therapy currently available. After analyzing the data, the great clinical benefits of the combined medico-surgical approach have been confirmed.

Average pregnancy rates after laparoscopic surgery reported in the literature are thus approximately 42 and 50% after combined medico-laparoscopic surgical treatment.

Conclusion

The present review of the literature leads us to conclude that a consensus will probably never be reached on minimal and mild endometriosis. Nevertheless, because the Canadian study reported a large number of cases, we strongly support the view that visible endometriosis must be removed at the time of surgery.

In cases of moderate and severe endometriosis-associated infertility, the combined approach (operative laparoscopy with GnRH-a) must be considered as the 'first-line' treatment. The mean pregnancy rate of 50% reported in the literature following surgery provides scientific proof that operative treatment should first be undertaken to give our patients the best chance of conceiving naturally. IVF is only indicated as a second-line treatment. In our department, after two IVF cycles, we have managed to obtain a pregnancy rate of approximately 61%. Thus, today it seems possible, by a combination of surgery and IVF, to offer the chance of pregnancy to up to 80% of women with endometriosis-associated infertility.

References

1 Donnez J, Chantraine F, Nisolle M: The efficacy of medical and surgical treatment of endometriosis-associated infertility: arguments in favour of a medico-surgical approach. Hum Reprod Update 2002;8:89–94.
2 Winkel CA: A cost-effective approach to the management of endometriosis. Curr Opin Obstet Gynecol 2000;12:317–320.
3 Minjarez DA, Schlaff WD: Update on the medical treatment of endometriosis. Obstet Gynecol Clin North Am 2000;27:641–651.
4 Wheeler JM, Malinak LR: Recurrent endometriosis: incidence, management and prognosis. Am J Obstet Gynecol 1983;146:247–253.
5 Telimaa S, Ronnberg L, Kauppila A: Placebo-controlled comparison of danazol and high-dose medroxyprogesterone acetate in the treatment of endometriosis after conservative surgery. Gynecol Endocrinol 1987;1:363–371.
6 Miller JD, Shaw RW, Casper RF, Rock JA, Thomas EJ, Dmowski WP, Surrey E, Malinak LR, Moghissi K: Historical prospective cohort study of the recurrence of pain after discontinuation of treatment with danazol or a gonadotropin-realeasing hormone agonist. Fertil Steril 1998;70:293–296.
7 Hornstein MD, Hemmings R, Yuzpe AA, Heinrichs WL: Use of nafarelin versus placebo after reductive laparoscopic surgery for endometriosis. Fertil Steril 1997;68:860–864.
8 Waller KG, Shaw RW: Gonadotropin-releasing hormone analogues for the treatment of endometriosis: long-term follow-up. Fertil Steril 1993;59:511–515.
9 Donnez J, Nisolle-Pochet M, Clerckx-Braun F, Sandow J, Casanas-Roux F: Administration of nasal Buserelin as compared with subcutaneous Buserelin implant for endometriosis. Fertil Steril 1989;52:27–30.
10 Nisolle M, Casanas-Roux F, Donnez J: Immunohistochemical analysis of proliferative activity and steroid receptor expression in peritoneal and ovarian endometriosis. Fertil Steril 1997;68:912–919.
11 Nisolle-Pochet M, Casanas-Roux F, Donnez J: Histologic study of ovarian endometriosis after hormonal therapy. Fertil Steril 1988;49:423–426.
12 Donnez J, Nisolle-Pochet M, Casananas-Roux F: Endometriosis-associated infertility: evaluation of preoperative use of danazol, gestrinone, and buserelin. Int J Fertil 1990;35:297–301.
13 Donnez J, Nisolle M, Gillerot S, Anaf V, Clerckx-Braun F, Casanas-Roux F: Ovarian endometrial cysts: the role of gonadotropin-releasing hormone agonist and/or drainage. Fertil Steril 1994;62:63–66.
14 Donnez J, Nisolle M, Squifflet J, Smets M: Laparoscopic treatment of rectovaginal adenomyosis; in Donnez J, Nisolle M (eds): An Atlas of Operative laparoscopy and Hysteroscopy. Carnforth, UK, Parthenon Publishing, 2001, pp 83–92.
15 Koninckx PR, Martin DC: Deep endometriosis: A consequense of infiltration or retraction or possibly adenomyosis externa? Fertil Steril 1992;58:924–928.
16 Donnez J, Nisolle M, Gillerot S, Smets M, Bassil S, Casanas-Roux F: Rectovaginal septum adenomyotic nodules: a series of 500 cases. Br J Obstet Gynaecol 1997;104:1014–1018.
17 Marcoux S, Maheux R, Berube S, and the Canadian Collaborative Group on Endometriosis: Laparoscopic surgery in infertile women with minimal or mild endometriosis. N Engl J Med 1997;337:217–222.
18 Parazzini F, and the Gruppo Italiano per lo Studio dell'Endometriosis: Ablation of lesions or no treatment in minimal-mild endometriosis in infertile women: a randomized trial. Hum Reprod 1999;14:1332–1334.
19 Donnez J, Smoes P, Gillerot S, Casanas-Roux F, Nisolle M: Vascular endothelial growth factor (VEGF) in endometriosis. Hum Reprod 1998;13:1686–1690.
20 Anaf V, Simon P, El Nakadi I, Fayt I, Buxant F, Simonart T, Peny MO, Noel JC: Relationship between endometriotic foci and nerves in rectovaginal endometriotic nodules. Hum Reprod 2000;15:1744–1750.
21 Donnez J, Nisolle M, Squifflet J: Ureteral endometriosis: a complication of rectovaginal endometriotic (adenomyotic) nodules. Fertil Steril 2002;77:32–37.
22 Donnez J, Lemaire-Rubbers M, Karaman Y, Nisolle-Pochet M, Casanas-Roux F: Combined (hormonal and microsurgical) therapy in infertile women with endometriosis. Fertil Steril 1987;48:239–242.
23 Donnez J, Nisolle M, Gillet N, Smets M, Bassil S, Casanas-Roux F: Large ovarian endometriomas. Hum Reprod 1996;11:641–646.
24 Donnez J, Nisolle M: L'endométriose péritonéale, le kyste endométriotique ovarien et le nodule de la lame rectovaginale sont trois pathologies différentes (éditorial). Références en Gynécologie Obstétrique 1995;3:121–123.
25 Serov SF, Scully RE, Sobin LH: Histological typing of ovarian tumors. Geneva: World Health Organization, International Histological Classification of Tumors 1973;9:17–21.
26 Motta PM, Van Blerkom J, Mekabe S: Changes in the surface morphology of ovarian germinal epithelium during the reproductive life and in some pathological conditions. Submicroscopy Cytol 1992;99:664–667.
27 Nisolle M: Peritoneal, ovarian and rectovaginal endometriosis are three distinct entities. (Thèse d'Agrégation de l'Enseignement Supérieur). Louvain (Belgium), Université Catholique de Louvain, 1996.
28 Nisolle M, Donnez J (eds): Peritoneal, Ovarian and Rectovaginal Endometriosis: The Identification of Three Separate Diseases. Carnforth, UK, Parthenon Publishing, 1996.
29 Rosenfeld DL, Lecher BD: Endometriosis in a patient with Rokitansky-Kuster-Hauser syndrome. Am J Obstet Gynecol 1981;139:105.
30 Donnez J: CO_2 laser laparoscopy in infertile women with endometriosis and women with adnexal adhesions. Fertil Steril 1987;48:390–394.
31 Brosens IA, Van Ballaer P, Puttemans P, Deprest J: Reconstruction of the ovary containing large endometriomas by an extraovarian endosurgical technique. Fertil Steril 1996;66:517–521.
32 Audebert A, Descamps P, Marret H, Ory-Lavollee L, Bailleul F, Hamamah S: Pre- or post-operative medical treatment with nafarelin in stage III–IV endometriosis: a French multicenter study. Eur J Obstet Gynecol Reprod Biol 1998;79:145–148.
33 Johnson KM: Endometriosis. The case for early, aggressive treatment. J Reprod Med 1998; 43(suppl 3):309–315.
34 Schindler AE, Buhler G, Lubben G, Kienle E: What is the value of combined surgical-hormonal therapy of endometriosis management? Zentralbl Gynaekol 1998;120:183–190.

General References

Adamson GD, Pasta DJ: Surgical treatment of endometriosis-associated infertility: meta-analysis compared with survival analysis. Am J Obstet Gynecol 1994;171:1488–1504.

Busacca M, Bianchi S, Agnoli B, Candiani M, Calia C, De Marinis S, Vignali M: Follow-up of laparoscopic treatment of stage III–IV endometriosis. J Am Assoc Gynecol Laparosc 1999;6:55–58.

Crosignani PG, Rubin BL, and The ESHRE Capri Workshop Group: Optimal use of infertility diagnostic tests and treatments. Hum Reprod 2000;15:723–732.

Chang FH, Chou HH, Soong YK, Chang MY, Lee CL, Lai YM: Efficacy of isotopic $^{13}CO_2$ laser laparoscopic evaporation in the treatment of infertile patients with minimal to mild endometriosis: a life table cumulative pregnancy rates study. J Am Assoc Gynecol Laparosc 1997;4:219–223.

Hughes EG, Fedorkow DM, Collins JA: A quantitative overview of controlled trials in endometriosis-associated infertility. Fertil Steril 1993; 59:963–970.

Nisolle M, Donnez J: Peritoneal endometriosis, ovarian endometriosis, and adenomyotic nodules of the rectovaginal septum are three different entities. Fertil Steril 1997;68:585–596.

Pagidas K, Falcone T, Hemmings R, Miron P: Comparison of reoperation for moderate (stage III) and severe (stage IV) endometriosis-related infertility with in vitro fertilization-embryo transfer. Fertil Steril 1996;65:791–795.

Pouly JL, Drolet J, Canis M, Boughazine S, Mage G, Bruhat MA, Wattiez A: Laparoscopic treatment of symptomatic endometriosis. Hum Reprod 1996;11(suppl 3):67–88.

Rana N, Thomas S, Rotman C, Dmowski WP: Decrease in the size of ovarian endometriomas during ovarian suppression in stage IV endometriosis. Role of preoperative medical treatment. J Reprod Med 1996;41:348–392.

Sutton CJ, Ewen SP, Jacobs SA, Whitelaw NL: Laser laparoscopic surgery in the treatment of ovarian endometriomas. J Am Assoc Gynecol Laparosc 1997;4:319–323.

Wheeler JM, Knittel JD, Miller JD: Depot leuprolide versus danazol in treatment of women with symptomatic endometriosis. Am J Obstet Gynecol 1992;167:1367–1371.

Soong YK, Chang FH, Chou HH, Chang MY, Lee CL, Lai YM, Chang SY: Life table analysis of pregnancy rates in women with moderate or severe endometriosis comparing danazol therapy after carbon dioxide laser laparoscopy plus electrocoagulation or laparotomy plus electrocoagulation versus danazol therapy only. J Am Assoc Gynecol Laparosc 1997;4:225–230.

Post-Presentation Discussion

Professor Terakawa: Thank you, Professor Donnez for that very nice and informative presentation. This paper is now open for discussion.

Dr. Suginami: Professor Donnez, I almost completely agree with the information you have presented, except for your separation of peritoneal lesions from adenomyotic lesions. You suggest that there is no interaction between these two lesions. If I may make a comment on this, if you look at the average age of patients with adenomyotic lesions, it is relatively high. Could you give us the age of the youngest patient in your experience with an adenomyotic lesion?

Professor Donnez: Unfortunately, in our department, the youngest was 21 years old. We have a series so far of 1,500 cases of retroperitoneal nodules in my department alone, and as you know, Philip Koninckx, who is 30 km to the north of my university, in the Flemish part of the country, has nearly 800 cases. This means essentially that we have the highest prevalence in the world, and we were surprised to see that among patients presenting with an adenomyotic nodule, the average age was becoming younger and younger, with the majority of patients being between 25 and 35 years of age. I think it is really a new disease. I cannot believe that 20 years ago we simply missed this type of pathology.

Dr. Suginami: I agree, but I believe that you would also agree that there is a group of younger women who have peritoneal lesions without adenomyotic lesions.

Professor Donnez: Yes, I fully agree with that. We don't know why this is the case, but there may be a genetic basis for it. I will discuss this in greater detail later, but peritoneal lesions are caused by reflux of menstrual debris, while adenomyotic disease is provoked by something else, possibly related to the environment. I am not sure about the situation in Japan, but please remember that at least in Europe and in the United States, diethylstilbestrol was prescribed for years and years to the mother during pregnancy to avoid miscarriage. It took 20 years before we were able to understand that the diethylstilbestrol given to the mother at the beginning of the pregnancy was capable of provoking clear cell adenocarcinoma in the same area. So far, there has been no cancer described, at least in my series. But I just read two papers yesterday describing cases of adenocarcinoma originating from an adenomyotic nodule in the rectovaginal space.

I accept the concept of peritoneal endometriosis, and ovarian endometriosis, as being intraperitoneal endometriosis. And I think that retroperitoneal adenomyotic disease, which can be mixed with some peritoneal lesions, is another entity. We are now trying to understand the difference, and we need to have more and more data. We need to use microarray differentiation, but this procedure costs a lot of money. I hope that Japanese research gynecologists like yourselves will also be able to concentrate more and more on researching this differentiation.

Professor Kanzaki: You mentioned that the adenomyotic lesion beneath the peritoneum did not respond to the GnRH agonist or to oral contraceptives. But aromatase inhibitor may be used in the future, and perhaps you can have some expectation as to its usefulness. How do you explain the mechanism underlying the effectiveness of this type of treatment?

Professor Donnez: It's like in fibroids. Because of the presence of aromatase, there needs to be the possibility that estradiol is created in the lesion itself, to promote growth whatever the level is of circulating estrogens. In 1998, one of the first papers on this issue was published by Takayama in *Fertility and Sterility* describing a case of a postmenopausal woman who had undergone bilateral oophorectomy and had no hormonal replacement therapy. She had a large nodule in the rectovaginal septum after hysterectomy. Although it was not published as such, it was actually a nodule of the rectovaginal septum, and it was growing and growing. Finally, this Japanese doctor gave aromatase inhibitor, and a nearly complete disappearance of the nodule was achieved. That was the first publication of the efficacy of an aromatase inhibitor. Thus, we can guess about the efficacy of this treatment, but we have to prove this by further study, which is the next step forward in research. In fact, there are two possibilities for the future: 1) GnRH agonist orally, which can modulate and obtain the therapeutic window for each patient, and 2) aromatase inhibitors.

Professor Kanzaki: So you recommend controlling the local production of estrogen. Should this be done systemically or locally?

Professor Donnez: At the present time, I would have to say both, because I have no idea what is the most effective approach. The goal of the prospective study that we have to initiate is to determine this.

Professor Terakawa: I would have to say that the concept of a therapeutic window is just based on speculation by Dr. Barbieri. He just gave this report at a sponsored symposium in the United States, and we don't have data to demonstrate that between 30–50 pg/ml estradiol does not induce growth of endometriotic cells.

Professor Donnez: I fully agree. The concept of a therapeutic window must be proven in the future by two things: the clinical aspect, namely the absence of symptoms, and by the biological and histological aspect, namely the absence of growth.

Professor Taketani: I am interested in discussing the management of younger women; for example, a patient who is single, and mostly asymptomatic, but who has a large ovarian cyst, either unilaterally or bilaterally. In such a case, we might like to consider further fertility preservation. However, the earlier the treatment is performed, the higher is the risk of recurrence. Thus, there is a dilemma in how to manage such cases.

Professor Donnez: You raise a very important point, because as mentioned by another discussant, more and more young women have peritoneal endometriosis and ovarian endometriosis. I'm sure you would agree that 10 years ago, there were no women less than 20 years of age with ovarian endometriomas. Now, in 2002, it is not surprising to see such cases involving 17- and 18-year-old women. We manage these young patients exactly as we would an adult, even if they are in adolescence. We treat by drainage, followed by coagulation of the internal wall. If you do bilateral ovarian cystectomy, there is a risk of damaging the normal ovarian cortex. The recurrence rate is only 6%. Thus, drainage and GnRH agonist are used, followed three months later by vaporization. And then, because this patient is very young, we will ask her to remain in amenorrhea until the time she desires to get pregnant. The best approach is to convince her to take progestogens continuously. This is the only way to prevent the recurrence of endometriosis, since we assume that some endometriosis, like peritoneal endometriosis and ovarian endometriosis, can be provoked by the reflux of menstrual debris.

Professor Taketani: So you mean that postoperative therapeutic, long-lasting medication, such as progestogens, may be effective in preventing recurrence?

Professor Donnez: I am quite sure that they are. It could be that in the future it will be something else. Long-term therapy must be clearly separated from the 'attack', or first-line medical therapy. The most active drugs are surely GnRH agonists, but because of side effects like osteoporosis, the association of GnRH agonist plus tibolone, or of GnRH agonist plus some small amount of estrogens can be proposed. In my country, we treat the patient for a maximum of 6 months, because GnRH agonists are quite expensive, and thus we prefer to treat with GnRH agonists for three months, and then continue with progestogens, or an oral contraceptive. But with oral contraceptives, don't forget that she will menstruate every month. We prefer to ask very young women to be completely in amenorrhea.

Professor Taketani: But it's very difficult to maintain the suppression of menstruation using progestogen alone.

Professor Donnez: Yes, in our country, we use either medroxyprogesterone acetate 5 mg or lynestrenol 5 mg, which is a drug that is not expensive at all for the patient or for the health care insurance system. That is also a very important factor that we have to consider.

Professor Taketani: I totally agree with you on that point.

Dr. Obata: It has been reported that malignant transformation of endometriomas is 0.5–0.9%, and we need to carefully diagnose between endometriomas and ovarian carcinoma. So we perform laparoscopic surgery in cases of endometriomas without vegetations in the ovarian cysts and under 10 cm. I presume that this is also the indication for laparoscopic surgery for ovarian endometriomas in your hospital.

Professor Donnez: The goal of my lecture was to discuss endometriosis in infertility-associated endometriosis cases. What I have said here today is relevant for women less than 40 years of age. And so far in my series, I have not seen one case of adenocarcinoma associated with endometriomas in a woman less than 40 years old. That would be my first point. Secondly, as all equipment for echography in Europe is made in Japan, I am assuming that all Japanese women with endometriomas will have a vaginal echography done by an expert. And if there is a septum of intracystic vegetations, it should be treated as an ovarian cyst suspected to be malignant. I am speaking about well-defined endometriomas containing chocolate fluid without vegetations in women less than 40 years old. In women between 40 and 50 years of age, if the endometrioma is unilateral and 4–5 cm, we will remove the ovary by laparoscopy to avoid any contamination in the event that there was adenocarcinoma. But the prevalence of adenocarcinoma around menopause in an endometrioma is less than 1%, and the endometrial carcinoma cases that were described by Nezhat at the level of an ovarian endometrioma and adenoma concern women more than 52 years old. That makes sense. We're not speaking about the same group of patients when we speak of women in their thirties with infertility as opposed to postmenopausal women with ovarian cysts. We know that the risk of adenocarcinoma is much higher in the latter group, and we have to treat such postmenopausal women having an ovarian cyst bearing in mind that the cyst could be malignant. We must think differently when treating women less than 40 years old, those between 40 and 50, and women more than 50 years of age.

Professor Terakawa: One more question, Dr. Harada.

Dr. Harada: We are interested in the association between active red peritoneal lesions, and cytokine levels, such as interleukin 6 and TNF-α in the peritoneal fluid of patients with endometriosis. I think that you would agree that these active lesions might be related to the infertility associated with endometriosis. We know that medical treatment, such as GnRH agonist, reduces the number of active lesions and also the level of cytokines in the peritoneal fluid. Unfortunately, we do not have evidence that medical treatment enhances fertility or improves the pregnancy rate in endometriosis patients. Could you comment on that?

Professor Donnez: Yes, I think that what you have said demonstrates the need for an association between medical and surgical therapy. What would be informative, although impossible now from an ethical point of view, would be to conduct the following histological evaluation, as was commonly done in the past. If you do a cytokine evaluation in a patient with red lesions before treatment and then you give six months of GnRH therapy, at the end of the therapy, you can evaluate the peritoneal fluid. After GnRH therapy for one month, the amount of peritoneal fluid is only a few milliliters, because there is no ovarian activity. And probably all red lesions have become less active. But if you wait and don't treat by surgery, you will find by repeat laparoscopy nearly the same percentage of active lesions three months after the cessation of therapy as before therapy. This is because these red lesions are in fact very active, and they show high mitotic activity. Also, I think that in the future we will be able to use microarrays to differentiate among the endometriotic lesions. These probably contain very active cells. This is similar to ovarian cancer, where following chemotherapy, there is sometimes a decrease of nearly 80–90% of the tumor volume. But if you take a biopsy of the residual tumoral tissue, histology can detect in some cases very, very active lesions, where the chemotherapy has had no effect at all. There is a differentiation of the tissue, which becomes independent, and after three months, there is regrowth from these very active lesions. In my opinion, the same hypothesis could be applied in endometriosis and explain why medical therapy alone is probably not efficacious. Endometriosis is like a benign cancer, and you have to bear this in mind. I am sure that with all of the scientists gathered around the table here today, and with all the research possibilities for cytokines and microarrays that you represent, you will be able to make significant research advances in this field.

Professor Terakawa: So you would choose combination therapy, right?

Professor Donnez: Yes.

Dr. Suginami: At the very beginning of your lecture, you said that we should treat patients with endometriosis for their symptoms, and not for the disease. My question is, what is a symptom, *per se*, of an ovarian endometrioma? Does it have any symptoms or not?

Professor Donnez: We occasionally encounter patients with a large endometrioma without any symptoms, but often they are infertile. So the symptom in that case is infertility. If the patient comes to your clinic with infertility, no pain, but infertility ...

Dr. Suginami: That case is fine, but ...

Professor Donnez: But my point is that it is very rare. In our experience, there are not many patients who are fertile with bilateral endometriomas of more than 3 cm. If she has a 2-cm endometrioma on one side, no symptoms, and is able to get pregnant, I won't touch the endometrioma. I only treat the symptoms. If she comes to my clinic with bilateral endometriomas and infertility, I will treat her. If she comes in postpartum to ask for the pill, and at that point I discover an endometrioma on one side of 2 cm, I leave it alone. I don't perform surgery. But this last example is really infrequent because most women with endometriosis are infertile.

Dr. Suginami: How about leakage of the fluid, the content of the endometrioma?

Professor Donnez: Yes, but I have never seen rupture of an endometrioma of less than 3 cm. Systematically, if the endometrioma is 3 cm or larger, I will propose resection involving vaporization of the endometrioma to avoid rupture, because if a rupture occurs, it will cause a lot of pelvic adhesions and sometimes the results are disastrous.

Session 2
Review

Gynecologic and Obstetric Investigation

Gynecol Obstet Invest 2002;54(suppl 1):11–17
DOI: 10.1159/000066289

Investigation of the Localization of Nerves in the Uterosacral Ligament: Determination of the Optimal Site for Uterosacral Nerve Ablation

Miho Fujii[a] Satoru Sagae[a] Toshio Sato[b] Mizuyo Tsugane[b] Gen Murakami[b] Ryuichi Kudo[a]

Departments of [a]Gynecology and Obstetrics and [b] Anatomy, Sapporo Medical University School of Medicine, Sapporo, Japan

Key Words
Immunohistochemistry · Nerve staining · Laparoscopic uterosacral ligament nerve ablation · Dysmenorrhea

Abstract
We select surgical treatment for cases for which severe dysmenorrhea persists following medical treatment. Many reports have described the use of neurectomies by cutting off pain conducting nerve pathways using laparoscopic surgery. Laparoscopic uterosacral nerve ablation (LUNA) has been associated with a high success rate for pain control, but there are few reports of anatomical studies in the uterosacral ligament. Using an immunohistochemical method, we examined the number and types of nerve fiber bundles in the uterosacral ligaments and its surrounding tissue in cadavers. The greatest number of nerve fiber bundles was found at a distance of 16.5–33 mm and at a depth of 3–15 mm distal to the site of attachment of the uterosacral ligament to the uterine cervix. Furthermore, there were many more sympathetic and parasympathetic nerve fiber bundles than sensory ones in the uterosacral ligament and its surrounding tissue. These results show the appropriate site of transection of uterosacral ligaments when performing LUNA.

Introduction

Dysmenorrhea can be divided into two types, organic or functional dysmenorrhea, depending on the presence of organic diseases, such as endometriosis and uterine myoma. Both types of dysmenorrhea cause disturbances to daily life, and active treatment is required. The first choice of treatment for organic dysmenorrhea is treatment addressing the underlying disorder, whereas the first choice of conservative treatment for functional dysmenorrhea is the relief of pain by nonsteroidal anti-inflammatory drugs (NSAIDs) or hormone therapy aimed at suppressing ovulation. Medical treatment with a gonadotropin-releasing hormone agonist, Danazol, progesterone and oral contraceptives (OC) are used for women with endometriosis who wish to preserve future fertility, and these medical treatments for women with functional dysmenorrhea are used if symptoms are aggravated. However, 20–25% of women with dysmenorrhea do not respond to pain-relieving drug therapy [1, 2], and thus surgical treatment must be considered for such cases.

Among various surgical treatments for dysmenorrhea, there have been many reports on the successful use of operations, particularly transection of the uterosacral ligament, to cut off the pelvic pain pathway. However, there has been little anatomical examination on the proper site for nerve ablation. In the present study, in order to deter-

KARGER

Fax + 41 61 306 12 34
E-Mail karger@karger.ch
www.karger.com

Accessible online at:
www.karger.com/goi

Satoru Sagae, Associate Professor
Department of Obstetrics and Gynecology
Sapporo Medical University, School of Medicine
South 1 West 16, Chuou-ku, Sapporo 060-0061 (Japan)
Tel. +81 11 611 2111, ext. 3373, Fax +81 11 614 0860, E-Mail sagaes@sapmed.ac.jp

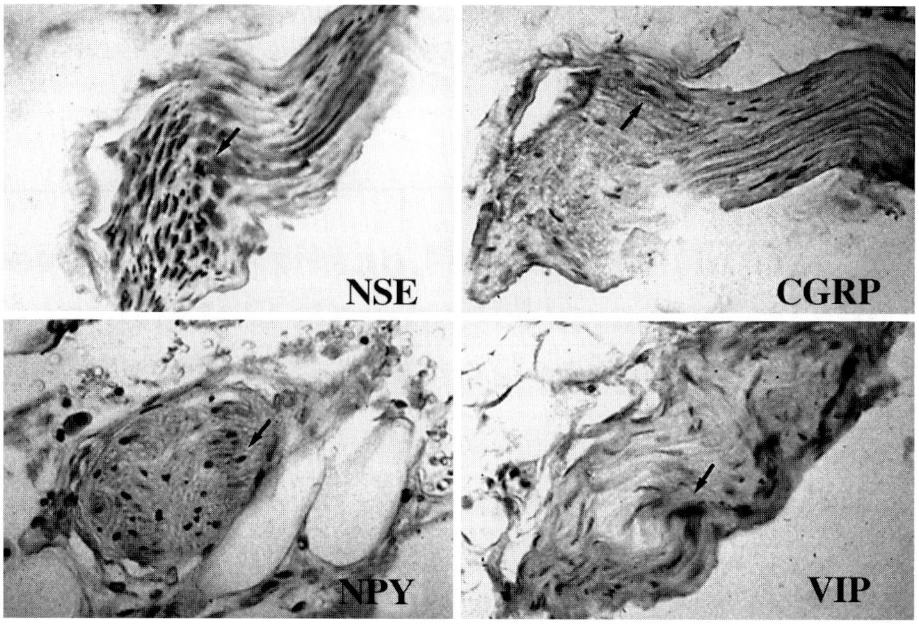

Fig. 1. Localization of four different proteins in nerve fiber bundles. Arrows indicate positive staining in nerve fiber bundles: upper left; NSE (neuron-specific enolase), upper right; CGRP (calcitonin gene-related peptide), lower left; NPY (neuropeptide tyrosine C-terminal flanking), lower right; VIP (vasoactive intestinal peptide).

mine the most effective site for nerve ablation, we investigated the density of nerve fiber bundles as well as the distribution of autonomous nerves and sensory nerves in the uterosacral ligament and its surrounding tissue using pelvic organs of the cadaver.

Methods

Preparation of Specimens

A large area of pelvic tissue including the uterus, uterosacral ligament, and parauterine connective tissue was resected *en bloc* from 10 cadavers, and the resected tissue was fixed in formalin. Slices of the uterosacral ligament of 8 μm in thickness, including tissues adjacent to the ligament, were cut at 1.5 mm intervals. Slices were obtained both until 4 cm in the left lateral direction from the site of attachment of the uterosacral ligament parallel to the sagittal plane and until 3 cm downward from the site of attachment of the uterosacral ligament parallel to the horizontal plane.

Immunohistochemical Staining for Different Nerve Fibers

Immunohistochemical staining of different kinds of nerve fibers was done using a rabbit polyclonal antibody to neuron-specific enolase (NSE) (DAKO, Denmark) [3], rabbit polyclonal antibody to neuropeptide tyrosine (NPY), C-terminal flanking peptide (C-PON) (Affinity Research Products Co. Ltd, UK) [4], rabbit polyclonal antibody to vasoactive intestinal peptide (VIP) (Biogenesis Co. Ltd, UK) [5] and rabbit polyclonal antibody to calcitonin gene-related peptide (CGRP) (Sigma, USA) [6] as primary antibodies and a HISTOFINE SAB-PO kit (Nichirei, Japan) for secondary antibodies. NSE staining was used for identification of all nerve fibers, and NPY, VIP and CGRP stainings were used for identification of the sympathetic nerve fibers, parasympathetic nerve fibers, and sensory nerve fibers, respectively. NSE-, NPY-positive nerves were identified as sympathetic, NSE-, VIP-positive nerves as parasympathetic, and NSE-, CGRP-positive as sensory nerves.

Calculation of Nerve Fiber Bundles

A thin plastic board with 5 mm square holes was placed on top of the immunohistochemically stained specimen, and the number of nerve fiber bundles was counted for each square. The total numbers of NSE-, NPY-, VIP- and CGRP-positive nerve fiber bundles were calculated in each slice. The numbers of positive nerve fiber bundles were calculated for specimens from each of 10 cadavers, and mean values for each were obtained. Slices from each specimen were lined up in the order they had been cut, and the mean total number of nerve fiber bundles and the ratios of NPY-, VIP- and CGRP-positive nerve fiber bundles to the total number of nerve fiber bundles were calculated for each cross-sectional region of each of the 10 cadavers.

Results

Findings of Immunohistochemical Staining

A difference was observed in the diameters of nerve fiber bundles depending on the location in the tissue. Some nerve fiber bundles were found alone while others were found together with blood vessels. In some sites, ganglia were seen as well as nerve fibers. NSE, NPY, VIP and CGRP stainings were seen cross-sectionally arranged in lamella in the nerve fiber bundle. Stainings of some vertically cut fibers appeared as spots, which were dependent on the cut surface (fig. 1).

Table 1. Number of nerve fiber bundles discriminated by immunohistochemical staining in each sagittal cross-sectional region distant from the attachment of the uterosacral ligament

Distance mm	NSE	NPY	VIP	CGRP
1.5	25.2	12.1	11.4	1.7
3.0	27.3	9.2	15.1	3.0
4.5	21.9	11.2	9.9	0.8
6.0	41.0	17.8	20.8	2.4
7.5	30.1	10.3	15.7	4.1
9.0	40.7	16.1	18.9	5.7
10.5	36.8	19.9	14.2	2.7
12.0	60.3	22.4	26.7	11.2
13.5	57.2	21.7	25.9	9.6
15.0	59.3	27.0	19.1	13.2
16.5	56.9	19.0	29.8	8.1
18.0	50.0	20.0	19.9	10.1
19.5	58.8	21.7	30.1	7.0
21.0	89.9	39.8	33.2	16.9
22.5	67.1	30.7	25.3	11.1
24.0	62.2	27.1	26.3	8.8
25.5	54.7	19.4	31.0	4.3
27.0	52.0	20.1	23.7	8.2
28.5	52.6	27.8	18.1	6.7
30.0	37.3	19.0	11.7	6.6
31.5	42.2	14.1	22.9	5.2
33.0	8.1	5.1	2.2	0.8
34.5	20.8	8.3	11.9	0.6
36.0	36.2	15.7	15.8	4.7
37.5	12.3	7.8	3.1	1.4
39.0	20.0	8.2	9.2	2.6
40.5	16.9	12.0	3.9	1.0
42.0	2.0	0.9	1.1	0.0
43.5	0.0	0.0	0.0	0.0

Table 2. Number of nerve fiber bundles discriminated by immunohistochemical staining in each horizontal cross-sectional region distant from the attachment of the uterosacral ligament

Distance mm	NSE	NPY	VIP	CGRP
1.5	18.1	6.4	8.9	2.8
3.0	25.3	10.9	12.2	2.2
4.5	14.6	5.3	6.4	2.9
6.0	27.9	10.1	12.1	5.7
7.5	39.0	18.2	15.1	5.7
9.0	35.4	13.8	14.1	7.5
10.5	28.2	12.3	9.9	6.0
12.0	33.2	12.7	14.3	6.2
13.5	36.5	14.2	16.7	5.6
15.0	40.4	15.4	18.1	6.9
16.5	35.9	16.6	14.2	5.1
18.0	30.3	15.0	9.4	5.9
19.5	37.1	16.2	14.7	6.2
21.0	27.4	9.8	10.3	7.3
22.5	25.7	9.6	11.5	4.6
24.0	22.1	10.8	9.4	1.9
25.5	23.6	9.4	10.7	3.5
27.0	27.9	11.5	13.4	3.0
28.5	18.1	6.3	8.1	3.7
30.0	20.4	9.7	7.7	3.0

Numbers of Nerve Fiber Bundles in Tissues

In sagittal sections of the uterosacral ligament and surrounding tissue, the number of nerve fiber bundles was calculated and the association between the number of nerve fiber bundles and the lateral distance from the uterus was determined. The number of nerve fiber bundles was the lowest at the site of attachment of the uterosacral ligament to the uterine cervix, and the highest at a section 16.5–33 mm laterally apart from the uterine cervix. This number decreased as the distance from the uterus increased (table 1).

In horizontal cross-sections in a downward direction from the site of attachment of the uterosacral ligament to the uterine cervix, more than 35 fiber bundles were found in sections from 3–15 mm in depth, and fewer fiber bundles were found in sections at depths of >15 mm (table 2).

Calculation of the ratios of NSE-, NPY-, VIP- and CGRP-positive nerve fiber bundles to total numbers in sagittal sections showed that VIP-positive nerve fiber bundles (parasympathetic) and NPY-positive one (sympathetic) were more numerous than CGRP-positive nerve fiber bundles (sensory) (fig. 2).

Discussion

Most operations to preserve the uterus are aimed at cutting off the pelvic nerves that conduct pain, and the site of resection is determined based on anatomical analysis of the courses of nerves in the pelvis. According to Counseller et al., the Th10-L1 sympathetic nerves are included in the hypogastric nerve, and they run along the vena cava inferior and the sacral bone, enter the pelvic cavity, and run inside the uterosacral ligament, and ultimately enter the uterus. On the other hand, the parasympathetic nerves from S1-S4 are included in the nerve erigentes, and they run for a short distance inside the uterosacral ligament in the lateral part of the pelvis and then

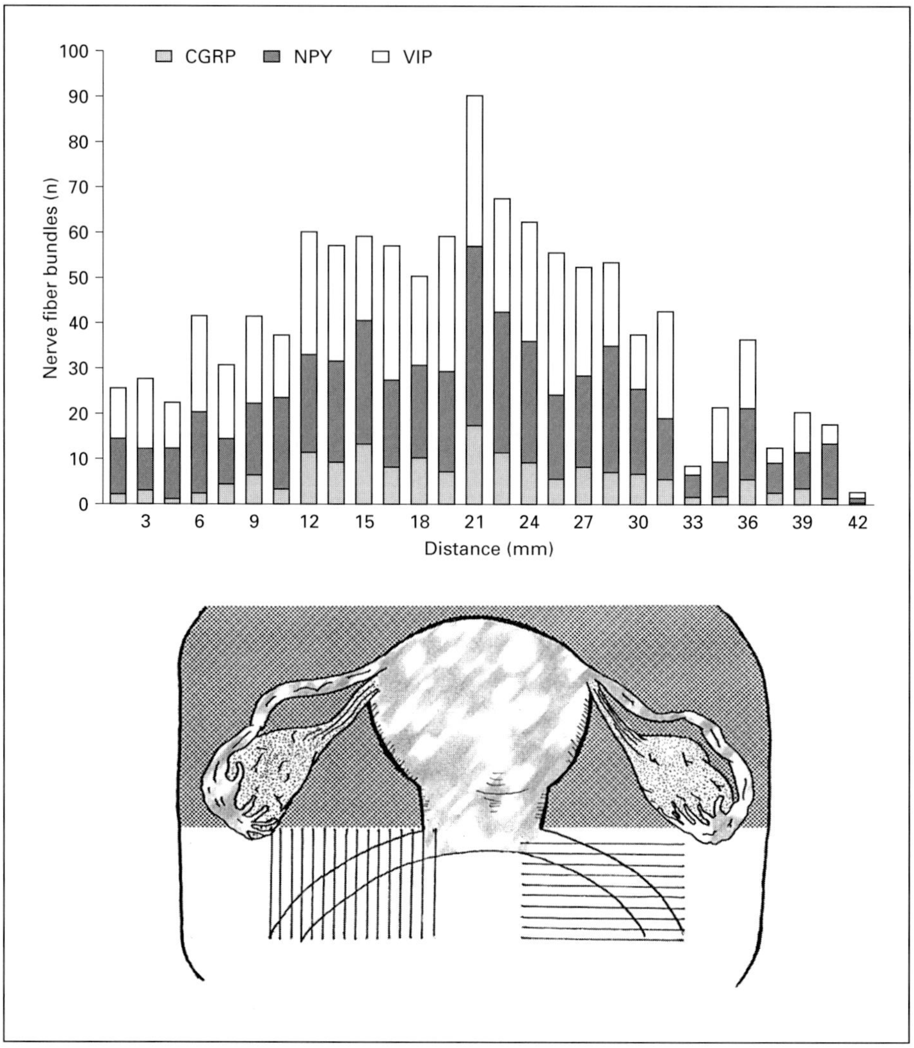

Fig. 2. Number of nerve fiber bundles classified by immunohistochemical staining. The graph shows number of nerve fiber bundles classified by positive staining of CGRP, NPY and VIP in each sagittal cross-sections every 15 mm distant from the site of attachment of the uterosacral ligament to the uterine cervix.

form ganglia on each side of the uterus (Frankenhauser ganglia) [7].

In terms of treatment modalities, and in particular surgical approaches, there are therefore two methods for cutting off pain-conducting nerve pathways in the pelvis: (1) presacral neurectomy involving cutting the Th10–L1 sympathetic nerves on the anterior surface of the sacrum bone [8], and (2) paracervical uterine denervation involving transection of the uterosacral ligament at its attachment to the uterus along with the above mentioned sympathetic nerves as well as the S1–S4 parasympathetic nerves, which transmit pain stimuli from the supravaginal region and to the uterine cervix [9].

Efficacies of presacral neurectomy have been described in many reports. Black et al. reported that presacral neurectomy is effective in 75–80% of dysmenorrhea cases [8]. Doyle et al. reported that improvement was seen in 95% of 73 cases of intractable dysmenorrhea treated by paracervical uterine denervation using either the abdominal or vaginal approach [9]. Furthermore, in recent years, there have been many reports on the use of these neurectomies by laparoscopic surgery, with success rates of 82% reported by Lichten [10] and similar high success rates reported by Perez [11] and other authors [12]. We have many reports about transection of the uterosacral ligament with relatively high success rate for dysmenorrhea. However, there are few detailed descriptions of the area of uterosacral ligaments to cut during paracervical uterine denervation. Campbell et al. reported in 1950 that the amount of nerve fibers in the uterosacral ligament differs according to the site of the ligament [13]. Although anatomical analysis of the distribution and density of nerve fibers surrounding the uterosacral ligament are important, there have been few reports since that of Campbell. The role of afferent fibers in dysmenorrhea is not clear, but this anatomical finding suggests that the site at which the uterosacral ligament is cut is very important for the outcome.

In the present study, the largest numbers of nerve fiber bundles and nerve cells were found at a distance 16.5–33 mm distal to the site of attachment of the uterosacral ligament to the uterine cervix at a depth of 3–15 mm. Most surgeons resect the uterosacral ligament in this region for the purpose of blocking the pain pathway, but the present findings confirmed that the area at this distance and depth is the most appropriate region anatomically. Furthermore, a relatively large number of nerve fiber bundles were found in horizontal sections at a depth of 15 mm, but an insufficient resection in depth of uterosacral ligament will cause an increased risk of later recurrence of dysmenorrhea. In the uterosacral ligament, different kinds of nerve bundles were distributed, such as sympathetic or parasympathetic or sensory ones. In our study, we detected very important findings of distribution of sensory nerves. It is well known that many nerve fibers are distributed extensively in the peritoneal surface as nerve endings. Many sensory nerves may exist as these free nerve endings. This is one reason for why the clinical efficacy of sufficient resection of the uterosacral ligament is sometimes low and there was a low ratio of sensory nerve fiber bundles to total nerve fiber bundles in the present study.

It has been shown that strong extension and convulsive contraction are stimuli that cause pain in hollow smooth muscle organs [14]. Some studies have discussed the possibility of treatment for dysmenorrhea via an administration of utero-relaxing substances. Bulleti suggested that β-adrenergic agonists might alleviate uterine discomfort accompanying dysmenorrhea [15]. Akerlund suggested that vasoconstrictive substances regulate the contractile activity of smooth muscles in vessel walls, and the administration of these substances causes myometrial hyperactivity and vasoconstriction with resultant uterine ischemia and pain [16]. Furthermore, Yen et al. reported on the efficacy of laparoscopic uterine nerve ablation (LUNA) when carrying out laparoscopic bipolar coagulation of uterine vessels (LBCUV). They suggested that LUNA might decrease postoperative ischemic pain and improve dysmenorrhea [17].

Our results identified a high ratio in the total number of sympathetic and parasympathetic nerve fiber bundles for the uterosacral ligament and surrounding tissue.

It is possible to understand the contribution to pain alleviation during menstruation by changing uterine contraction and vascularization of uterus.

In the present study, we investigated the anatomical localization and distribution of several different nerves in the uterosacral ligament and its surrounding tissue to determine the appropriate site of uterosacral ligament transection for cutting off pain-conduction pathways. Another pathway via nerve fibers traversing the infundibulopelvic ligaments that is concerned with lateral pain may also be present, given that resection of presacral nerves that innervate midline structures (the uterus and the cervix) alone does not remove the lateral pain.

Furthermore, quantitative and qualitative analysis of nerve fiber bundles may further our understanding of the mechanism of pain-onset in dysmenorrhea and produce new modalities, such as nerve plexus block for pain-control of long lasting dysmenorrhea.

References

1 Daywood YM: Premenstrual syndrome and dysmenorrhea. Baltimore, Urban& Schwarzenberg, 1985.
2 Henzl MR: Dysmennorrhea: Achievements and challenge. Sex Med Today 1985;9:8.
3 Seshi B, True L, Carter D, Rosai J: Immunohistochemical characterization of a set of monoclonal antibodies to human neuron-specific enolase. Am J Pathol 1988;131:258–269.
4 Figueroa JM, Mansilla E, Suburo AM: Innervation of nasal turbinate blood vessels in rhinitic and nonrhinitic children. Am J Respir Crit Care Med 1998;157:1959–1966.
5 Coppes MH, Marani E, Thomeer RT, Groen GJ: Innervation of 'painful' lumbar discs. Spine 1997;22:37–49.
6 Koo H, Heungshik SL, Young SN, Choong HL, Yeo SY, Tae-Cheon K, Moo HW: Immunohistochemical localization of substance P, Calcitonin gene-related peptide, galanin and calcium binding proteins in myenteric and submucosal plexuses of goat small intestine. Online J Vet Res 2002;1:7–28.
7 Counseller VS, Craig W: The treatment of dysmenorrhea by resection of the presacral nerves: Evaluation of endresults. Am J Obstet Gynecol 1934;28:161–167.
8 Black WT: Use of presacral sympathectomy in the treatment of dysmenorrhea. Am J Obstet Gynecol 1964;89:16–20.
9 Doyle JB: Paracervical uterine denervation by transection of the cervical plexus. Am J Obstet Gynecol 1955;70:1–16.
10 Lichten EM, Bombard J: Surgical treatment of primary dysmenorrhea with laparoscopic uterine nerve ablation. J Reprod Med 1987;32:37–41.

11 Perez JJ: Laparoscopic presacral neurectomy. Results of the first 25 cases. J Reprod Med 1990;35:625–630.
12 Fujii M, Liao Y, Mori S, Sagae S, Suzuki T, Endo T, Ito E, Kudo R: Uterosacral ligament transection for the relief of dysmenorrhea. J Gynecolog Tech 1997;3:157–162.
13 Campbell RM, Arbor A: The anatomy and histology of the sacrouterine ligaments. Am J Obstet Gynecol 1950;59:1–12.
14 Wolf S, Wolff HG: Pain arising from the stomach and mechanism underlying gastric symptoms. Res Publ Ass Res Nerv Ment Dis 1943; 23:289–301.
15 Bulletti C, de Ziegler D, de Moustier B, Polli V, Bolelli G, Franceschetti F, Flamigni C. Uterine contractility: Vaginal administration of the beta-adrenergic agonist, terbutaline. Evidence of direct vagina-to-uterus transport. Ann NY Acad Sci 2001:943:163–171.
16 Akerlund M: Vascularization of human endometrium. Uterine blood flow in healthy condition and in primary dysmenorrhea. Ann NY Acad Sci 1994:734:47–56.
17 Yen YK, Liu WM, Yuan CC, Ng HT: Addition of laparoscopic uterine nerve ablation to laparoscopic bipolar coagulation of uterine vessels for women with uterine myomas and dysmenorrhea. J Am Assoc Gynecol Laparosc 2001;8: 573–578.

Post-Presentation Discussion

Professor Fukaya: Thank you very much for your nice presentation, Dr. Fujii. In opening this up for discussion, I would like to ask you one question. For the operation, do you perform LUNA alone, or do you perform LUNA plus treatment of the endometrial lesion?

Dr. Fujii: Both LUNA and vaporization of the endometrial lesion.

Dr. Maeda: You described three different nerves in the uterosacral ligament, and noted that there are few sensory nerves. What do you think is the most important nerve for the cause of pelvic pain?

Dr. Fujii: As you can see, the immunohistochemical staining is not complete, and yet the sensory nerves account for only 20% of all nerves, but in endometriosis cases, blood supply to the uterus is very poor, and parasympathetic and sympathetic nerves were cut. I think the uterine blood supply is thereby changed. I believe this is also the reason why the dysmenorrhea and pain are removed by LUNA.

Professor Donnez: I would like to congratulate you on this interesting research; however, I don't think that the answer you give concerning the blood supply is correct, because the blood supply is coming laterally from the cardinal ligaments and from the uterine arteries, and as far as I know from anatomy, the uterine artery and the broad cardinal ligaments have their own sympathetic and sensory nerves. Thus, you are not changing the blood supply. However, a more interesting question is, in all these dissections that you have done, have you observed spread of endometrial cells into the nerves?

Dr. Fujii: No, I didn't observe endometriotic tissue.

Professor Donnez: This is probably because you are only examining a section. I'm quite sure that, like in breast cancer, you would be able to detect some endometrial cells in the nerves. You saw this during my lecture. The explanation in that case is that endometrial stromal cells have invaded through the nerves, causing the inflammatory reaction and pelvic pain. What you have done thus far is to just cut the uteral ligament, but as you know, there is reinnervation in six months to one year, and so what I would propose to you in order to continue with this interesting research, is to not only cut, but to resect deeply, both uteral ligaments, including the torus uterinum. This is the area of attachment between the uterosacral ligaments and the cervix. If you do the same study in this manner, I'm sure that you will soon be presenting a very interesting communication at the next World Congress of Endometriosis to be held in Maastricht in 2005.

Dr. Suginami: My question is quite similar to that of Professor Donnez. The point is how deeply and how widely do you dissect the ligament. That is a very important point, if you want to reduce the symptoms. In your lecture, you said that many nerve fibers are located in the adipose tissue, not in the uterosacral ligament. That is a very important point in that removal of that adipose tissue is very important for removing the symptoms. My question is how deeply and how widely do you dissect the uterosacral ligament. Also, do you dissect only the uterosacral ligament or do you dissect adipose tissue as well?

Dr. Fujii: I use cadavers for research, and when the human body is fixed in formalin for a long time, tissue shrinkage occurs. A depth of 15 or 20 mm is appropriate. I think it is better to cut at this depth than to just cut the ligament. It is better to remove the adjacent tissues, including fatty tissue. This is sufficient, whereas only cutting the ligament is not.

Professor Kanzaki: You said that the most effective cutting is at the area with the greatest abundance of nerve fibers. Is that correct? If so, I think that if we cut close to the uterine cervix, where the nerve fibers are concentrated, as you said, this would be the most effective approach.

Dr. Fujii: The distribution of sensory nerves and parasympathetic and sympathetic nerves is similar. The idea that there are some areas rich in sensory nerves and others rich in sympathetic nerves is not correct. All of the adjacent ligament tissues show the same concentration of sensory nerves, and sympathetic and parasympathetic nerves. To treat the pain effectively, it is better to cut at a sufficient depth, away from the uterine cervix, and in this way to include a very broad area.

Professor Kanzaki: So there are no areas where the nerve fibers are concentrated?

Dr. Fujii: That is correct.

Professor Kurachi: I cannot visualize what area you are describing when you refer to a sagittal section at around 2 cm distal to the uterine cervix. Is this area very close to the ureter?

Dr. Fujii: No, it is distant from ureter. But in real operations, we check the location of the ureter. However, this research is done on cadavers, and we don't have to check the location of the ureter.

Professor Donnez: You just need to manipulate the uterus. If you have a manipulator in the uterus, you can move it forward into an anteflexion position, and then you can easily recognize the uterosacral ligaments and the ureter. And by doing so, there is no risk of damaging the ureter. But take care if bleeding occurs. If you need to use bipolar coagulation, even though the ureter is 1 cm away, there is a risk of thermal damage. Thus, before coagulating the bleeding, I propose that you use a probe to clearly separate the ureter.

Dr. Fujii: I have a question for Professor Donnez. There are sympathetic nerve fibers and parasympathetic nerve fibers near the vessels. In terms of the mechanism of blood supply, I think the vessels control the blood supply to the uterus.

Professor Donnez: I propose that you continue your beautiful dissection so that it includes the entire cervix, including both the uterine and cervical arteries. You will probably find some connections between the splanchnic nerves of the uterosacral ligament, and some of the uterine artery nerves, which originated from lateral nerves, even the obturator nerves and other nerves.

Session 2
Original Article

Gynecologic and Obstetric Investigation

Gynecol Obstet Invest 2002;54(suppl 1):18–23
DOI: 10.1159/000066290

Is Endometriosis Really Associated with Pain?

Mikio Momoeda[a] Yuji Taketani[a] Naoki Terakawa[b] Hiroshi Hoshiai[c] Kenichi Tanaka[d] Osamu Tsutsumi[a] Yutaka Osuga[a] Masanori Maruyama[a] Tasuku Harada[b] Koushirou Obata[c] Kunihiko Hayashi[e]

[a]Department of Obstetrics and Gynecology, University of Tokyo, [b]Department of Obstetrics and Gynecology, Tottori University, Tottori, [c]Department of Obstetrics and Gynecology, Kinki University School of Medicine, Kinki, [d]Department of Obstetrics and Gynecology, Niigata University, Niigata, [e]School of Health Sciences, Gunma University, Gunma, Japan

Key Words
Endometriosis · Dysmenorrhea · Chronic pelvic pain · Dyspareunia · r-AFS classification · Cross-sectional study

Abstract
To address the contrasting findings regarding how pain is related to endometriosis, the relationship between pain and stage of endometriosis was dissected differently by the chief complaint to eliminate selection biases. A total of 1,092 women with endometriosis were classified into two groups depending on their chief complaint, i.e., infertility (infertility group; n = 476) or pain (pain group; n = 616). The correlations between disease stage and various types of pain were analyzed differently in each group. The frequencies of chronic pelvic pain and dyspareunia increased with disease stage either in the infertility group, in the pain group or in the aggregate. On the other hand, no significant relation between the severity of dysmenorrhea and disease stage was observed in the aggregate. Interestingly, a parallel increase in the severity of dysmenorrhea with disease stage was observed in the infertility group, but not in the pain group. In view of selection biases involved in analyzing endometriosis associated with pain, these results could be seen to support the contention that chronic pelvic pain, dyspareunia and dysmenorrhea are in fact related to the extent of endometriosis.

Introduction

Pain is a cardinal symptom of endometriosis. However, some patients with minimal endometriosis complain of severe dysmenorrhea, whereas extensive pathologic conditions can be incidentally found in asymptomatic women. Several clinical studies conducted to date have provided contradictory conclusions regarding the relation between pain and disease stage [1–4]. This raises the question whether pain is really associated with the pathophysiology of endometriosis per se. In practice, the presence of endometriosis is, in most instances, evaluated in women with complaints of pelvic pain and/or infertility. Given a variety of putative causes for pelvic pain, as well as pain in the setting of a normal appearing pelvic cavity, endometriosis found in women with pelvic pain cannot be interpreted a priori to mean that the lesions are responsible for the pain. With this in mind, we hypothesized that the link between pain and endometriosis could differ between affected women having pain versus those

KARGER
Fax + 41 61 306 12 34
E-Mail karger@karger.ch
www.karger.com

0378–7346/02/0545–0018$18.50/0

Accessible online at:
www.karger.com/goi

Mikio Momoeda, MD
Department of Obstetrics and Gynecology, University of Tokyo
7-3-1 Hongo, Bunkyo-ku
Tokyo 113-8655 (Japan)
Tel. +81 3 5800 8657, Fax +81 3 3816 2017, E-Mail momoeda-tky@umin.ac.jp

with infertility as the chief complaint. To test this, we investigated the relation of pain to endometriosis by the chief complaint, using data obtained from a nationwide multicenter cross-sectional survey.

Materials and Methods

In October 1997, we conducted a cross-sectional survey to estimate the number of cases of endometriosis in Japan, and demonstrated that the number of patients was approximately 128,200. In the present study, we selected 1,092 women with an established diagnosis of endometriosis by use of laparoscopy or laparotomy. The mean age of the women was 34.7 years, and the range was from 16 to 56. The patients were staged according to the revised American Fertility Society (r-AFS) classification, and classified into two groups depending on their chief complaint, i.e., infertility (infertility group) or pain (pain group). The severity of dysmenorrhea was graded as follows: none: no pain, mild: pain tolerable without analgesics, moderate: pain which can be controlled by analgesics, and severe: pain which cannot be controlled even with the use of analgesics.

The correlation between severity of dysmenorrhea and disease stage was examined using Kruskal-Wallis analysis of variance. The correlations between incidences of chronic pelvic pain or dyspareunia and disease stage were analyzed using Pearson's chi-square test. The correlations of pain symptoms with three distinct endometriotic lesions, namely ovarian endometrial cysts, invasive lesions affecting the cul de sac and peritoneal implants, were evaluated by use of a multivariate logistic regression analysis.

Results

All cases were staged based on the r-AFS classification, the number of cases of each stage being as follows: stage I: 224, stage II: 278, stage III: 342 and stage IV: 248. The frequencies of chronic pelvic pain and dyspareunia in stage I, II, III and IV were 32.7, 42.3, 49.4 and 58.5%, and 19.8, 26.5, 30.0 and 42.4%, respectively, showing an increasing incidence in pain symptoms with disease stage. This held true when comparing the infertility group and the pain group differently (fig. 1, 2).

When the two groups were looked at together, no significant relation between the severity of dysmenorrhea and disease stage was noted. However, a parallel increase in the severity of dysmenorrhea with disease stage was observed when restricting the analysis to the infertility group, but not in the pain group (fig. 3).

Next, we asked whether respective pain symptoms (dysmenorrhea, chronic pelvic pain and dyspareunia) related to specific endometriotic lesions (ovarian endometrial cysts, invasive cul de sac lesions and peritoneal implants). The odds ratios of relation of distinct lesions for each symptom against asymptomatic cases used as

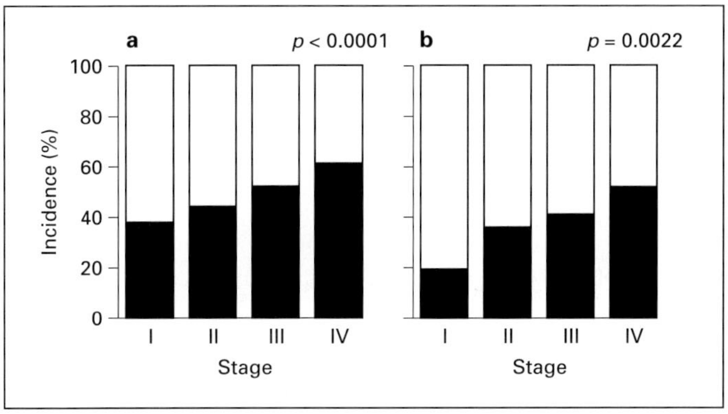

Fig. 1. Incidence of chronic pelvic pain in each stage of endometriosis. **a** Pain group. **b** Infertility group. All p values were calculated using Pearson's chi-square test.

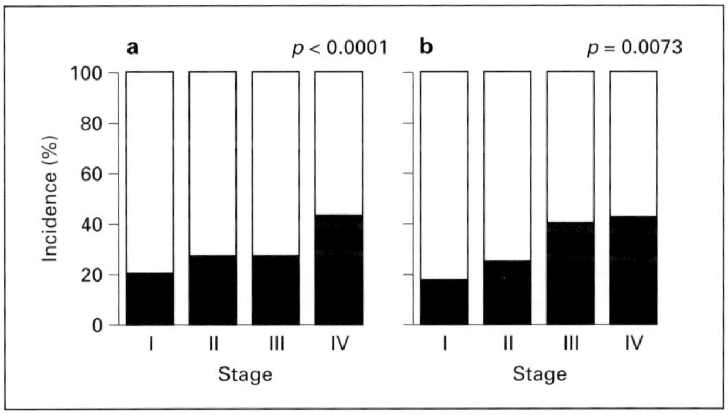

Fig. 2. Incidence of dyspareunia in each stage of endometriosis. **a** Pain group. **b** Infertility group. All p values were calculated using Pearson's chi-square test.

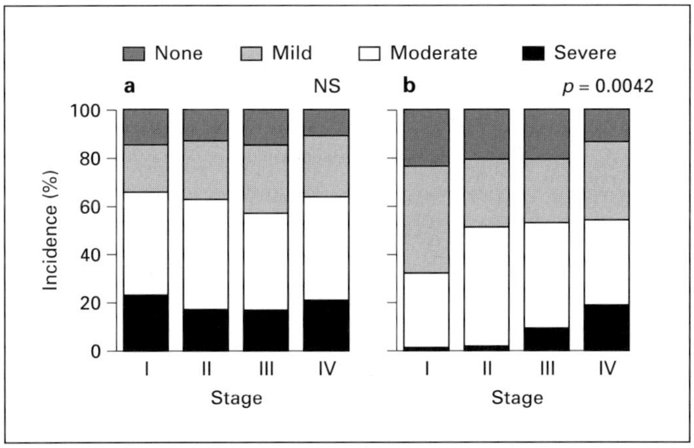

Fig. 3. Severity of dysmenorrhea in each stage of endometriosis. **a** Pain group. **b** Infertility group. All p values were calculated using Kruskal-Wallis analysis of variance.

Table 1. Odds ratios for endometriosis-related pain symptoms by lesion site

	Ovarian endometrial cysts	Cul de sac lesions	Peritoneal implants
Total cases			
Dysmenorrhea			
Mild	1.170	1.214	1.074
Moderate	1.045	1.738[a]	0.721
Severe	0.776	2.923[a]	0.820
Chronic pelvic pain	1.795[a]	2.390[a]	1.303[a]
Dyspareunia	1.269	3.075[a]	1.415[a]
Pain group			
Dysmenorrhea			
Mild	1.661	1.142	1.279
Moderate	1.074	1.217	1.045
Severe	0.705	1.721	1.468
Chronic pelvic pain	1.806[a]	2.227[a]	1.904[a]
Dyspareunia	1.156	2.774[a]	1.611[a]
Infertility group			
Dysmenorrhea			
Mild	1.124	1.614	1.375
Moderate	1.261	2.804[a]	0.750
Severe	1.945	10.253[a]	1.974
Chronic pelvic pain	1.907[a]	2.172[a]	1.638
Dyspareunia	1.487	3.652[a]	1.046

Odds ratios were evaluated by use of a multivariate logistic regression analysis.
[a] $p < 0.05$.

controls were calculated (table 1). When considering all cases together, moderate and severe dysmenorrhea were significantly related to invasive cul de sac lesions. Mild dysmenorrhea did not relate to any of the three lesions. This relation was observed when limiting the analysis to the infertility group, but not the pain group. Chronic pelvic pain correlated with the presence of all of the three lesions in both groups. Dyspareunia correlated with invasive cul de sac lesions in both groups, and peritoneal implants only in the pain group.

Discussion

Although pelvic pain and dyspareunia are thought to be characteristic of endometriosis, contrasting findings regarding the association of pain and its intensity with the stage and site of endometriosis have been reported [1–4]. One of the explanations for this may be that most studies looking into a link between pain and endometriosis have dealt with patients complaining of pain alone and other studies of patients irrespective of the type of symptom. It may be unarguable that the prevalence of pain in women with endometriosis and its severity in relation to the disease are confounded by the inclusion bias, that is, symptoms of patients enrolled.

In this paper, we demonstrated that chronic pelvic pain and dyspareunia, known symptoms caused by pelvic adhesions and deep endometriotic infiltration, are associated with the stage of endometriosis whatever the chief complaint of women with endometriosis. We further showed that dysmenorrhea is associated with stage only in cases complaining of infertility, but not pain.

Postulated mechanisms of endometriosis-associated pain are divided according to whether the pain is produced directly by endometriotic foci per se, or results from ensuing changes, such as adhesions, fibrosis, scarring, etc., that is, conditions that produce tension on tissues and organs or anatomical distortion [5]. In this study, we showed that chronic pelvic pain and dyspareunia are associated with endometriosis stage regardless of symptoms complained of, suggesting that these symptoms are causally related to the extent of the disease. This seems to make sense in that these symptoms are arguably generated by bowel fixity due to adhesions and scarring or nodularity and scarring of the uterosacral ligaments, findings that are essentially the same whether the chief complaint is pain or infertility. When looked at from another perspective, the findings obtained here serve to confirm the above notion.

By contrast, the severity of dysmenorrhea was shown to be related to disease stage in endometriosis sufferers complaining of infertility, but not of pain as the chief complaint. Dysmenorrhea occurs through mechanisms involving chemical or humoral mediators causing uterine hypercontractility or a variety of organic pathologies including endometriosis, adenomyosis, pelvic infection and adhesions, among other pathologies [6–8]. Furthermore, dysmenorrhea may result from stress and tension in a subset of women [9]. Endometriosis is thought to be the most common pathology for dysmenorrhea [10]. The precise mechanisms for this, however, are poorly understood. In light of both dysmenorrhea and endometriosis occurring at high frequencies, the two conditions may happen together. It follows that we cannot dissect the causal relationship between dysmenorrhea and endometriosis in an unbiased way when women complaining of pain are examined. On the other hand, when we investigate women seeking infertility treatment, less bias could be introduced in analyzing how dysmenorrhea relates to endometriosis. Viewed in this way, we favor the interpretation that the severity of dysmenorrhea is linked with the progression of endometriosis, a finding obtained by examining endometriosis sufferers with infertility as the chief complaint.

We further showed that dysmenorrhea was significantly associated with invasive cul de sac lesions, but not ovarian endometrial cysts and peritoneal implants. This may reflect the classification system employed that automatically places patients having severe cul de sac lesions in the most advanced category, i.e. stage IV. If so, it is still not certain whether the severity of dysmenorrhea parallels the progression of the disease or is just related to cul de sac lesions.

In summary, we provided data strongly supporting the contention that endometriosis-related pain symptoms, such as chronic pelvic pain, dyspareunia and dysmenorrhea, are all correlated with the stage of endometriosis, by analyzing women with endometriosis differently according to their chief complaint so as to minimize bias inevitably introduced in the setting of clinical studies on endometriosis.

Acknowledgement

This work was supported by a grant-in-aid for Science and Research from the Ministry of Health, Labour and Welfare of Japan in 1997. We are grateful to all of the members of the project from the 13 participating universities; University of Tokyo, Tottori University, Kinki University School of Medicine, Niigata University, Tokushima University, Gunma University, Keio University, Yokohama City University, Nagasaki University, Osaka University, Asahikawa Medical College, Tohoku University and Nagoya University, for their enormous contribution to this collaboration.

References

1 Gruppo Italiano per lo Studio dell'Endometriosi: Relationship between stage, site and morphological characteristics of pelvic endometriosis and pain. Hum Reprod 2001;16:2668–2671.
2 Thornton JG, Morley S, Lilleyman J, Onwude JL, Currie I, Crompton AC: The relationship between laparoscopic disease, pelvic pain and infertility; an unbiased assessment. Eur J Obstet Gynecol Reprod Biol 1997;74:57–62.
3 Vercellini P, Trespidi L, De Giorgi O, Cortesi I, Parazzini F, Crosignani PG: Endometriosis and pelvic pain: relation to disease stage and localization. Fertil Steril 1996;65:299–304.
4 Fedele L, Parazzini F, Bianchi S, Arcaini L, Candiani GB: Stage and localization of pelvic endometriosis and pain. Fertil Steril 1990;53:155–158.
5 MacLaverty CM, Shaw RW: Pelvic pain and endometriosis; in Shaw RW (ed): Endometriosis. Oxford, Blackwell Science, 1995, pp 112–146.
6 Koninckx PR, Oosterlynck D, D'Hooghe T, Meuleman C: Deeply infiltrating endometriosis is a disease whereas mild endometriosis could be considered a non-disease. Ann NY Acad Sci 1994;734:333–341.
7 Donnez J, Nisolle M, Casanas-Roux F, Bassil S, Anaf V: Rectovaginal septum, endometriosis or adenomyosis: laparoscopic management in a series of 231 patients. Hum Reprod 1995;10:630–635.
8 Porpora MG, Koninckx PR, Piazze J, Natili M, Colagrande S, Cosmi EV: Correlation between endometriosis and pelvic pain. J Am Assoc Gynecol Laparosc 1999;6:429–434.
9 Waller KG, Shaw RW: Endometriosis, pelvic pain, and psychological functioning. Fertil Steril 1995;63:796–800.
10 Mahmood TA, Templeton AA, Thomson L, Fraser C: Menstrual symptoms in women with pelvic endometriosis. Br J Obstet Gynaecol 1991;98:558–563.

Post-Presentation Discussion

Professor Fukaya: Thank you very much, Dr. Momoeda. This paper is now open for discussion.

Professor Donnez: Dr. Momoeda, how do you explain dysmenorrhea and dyspareunia in women without endometriosis? What is the whole disease?

Dr. Momoeda: In my presentation, I only discussed dysmenorrhea. Dyspareunia and chronic pelvic pain in these cases may be strongly related to organic disease. However, as for dysmenorrhea, there are a variety of causes, including functional disease. Thus, for example, there is stenosis of the cervical canal or morphological problems of the uterus.

Professor Donnez: Yes, I agree with you on that point. However, I am wondering about the association of deep dyspareunia and dysmenorrhea, and severe endometriosis. Have you encountered cases involving such patients without endometriosis? Is there an association of these two symptoms?

Dr. Momoeda: For this study, the data were taken from endometriotic women only. Thus, we did not investigate cases without endometriosis, and so I cannot answer that question.

Professor Donnez: To go further in your research, I think that you should recall a paper our group published in 1992 describing a woman without endometriosis and with pelvic pain. We systematically performed a biopsy of the uterosacral ligaments, blind, in patients who did not have endometriosis. We were able to detect non-visible endometriosis, just microscopic endometriosis, in nearly 10% of cases. Thus, you have to take this into account as well. I agree with you that it is very interesting, but you have to try to clearly explain dysmenorrhea and dyspareunia in women without endometriosis.

Dr. Kubota: I know that dysmenorrhea is not related to the severity of endometriosis, but I think that this includes some psychological factor. Do you look at, for example, age, or working women versus those who do not work, or some other psychological effect? Do you check these data?

Dr. Momoeda: No, the questionnaire we used did not examine the psychological effect, but it would be very interesting to do so.

Dr. Kubota: Do you think there is some contribution from this psychological effect?

Dr. Momoeda: I think that the psychological factor for dysmenorrhea is very important, and especially in the pain group. The early stage pain group includes such patients.

Professor Hoshiai: I have just a simple question. These data are probably based on the old American Fertility Society classifications. Is that correct? Thus, Professor Donnez asked you whether no endometriosis in this presentation refers to no endometriosis in the pelvic cavity. At this point, deep endometrioses are discrete. Your papers published in 1992 or 1993 were also probably done under the same conditions. Currently, we need to make a new classification on how to evaluate extraperitoneal endometriosis, and this matter requires further discussion. Could you comment on this?

Professor Donnez: I fully agree that non-visible retroperitoneal endometrioses are currently not explained by the classification. And as you mentioned, it is the American Fertility Society classification. I have been in classification meetings with the US people for years and years. The concept of red, black, and white lesions has been accepted, but so far, non-visible lesions of the retroperitoneum have not been included.

Having said that, I think that with improvements in magnetic resonance imaging, we will be able to detect more and more subtle retroperitoneal lesions and thereby explain the pain. We also should not forget that we can use two fingers, which are excellent tools for pelvic examination. I'm convinced that the gynecologists, at least in Europe, and certainly in my country, do not examine the patient very well. They don't mobilize the uterus. They also do not examine during menstrual bleeding. We do not go deeply enough to feel the endometriotic lesions. And I really hope that in the future, markers capable of detecting retroperitoneal endometriosis will be available. However, in the absence of more data, we were unable to add that to the classification.

I am sure that pelvic pain, dysmenorrhea, and deep dyspareunia can be explained by non-visible endometriosis. You understand very well that even foci of endometriosis less than 200 μm that produce cytokines or prostaglandin very close to the nerves will induce pelvic pain. It is exactly the same for endometriotic lesions. I am sure that some lesions of 200 μm are capable of inducing very severe pelvic pain and dyspareunia, but they are not visible at laparoscopy. And thus according to the American Fertility Society, they don't exist. We have to re-revise the classification. Professor John Rock, as president of The World Endometriosis Society, has promised to create a group to analyze pelvic pain and to come up with a new classification for pelvic pain that is unrelated to the American Fertility Society of Endometriosis. On the other hand, I agree with you that ovarian endometriomas are not related to pelvic pain. Nevertheless, if you have an endometrioma of 5 cm in a patient who has no pelvic pain and no dyspareunia, according to the classification, it would probably be in stage 3 or 4.

Dr. Momoeda: Can I ask Professor Donnez a question? What kind of treatment do you recommend for the invisible endometriosis? It's a very difficult problem.

Professor Donnez: As a first comment, I would say that when doing a laparoscopy in women complaining of pelvic pain, I am able to find some minimal lesions. Thus, I am convinced that laparoscopists are simply looking inside the pelvic cavity too quickly. You have to fill the pelvic cavity full of saline solution, and look under water using your scope. But you have to look very closely, at a distance of a few millimeters. Sometimes you will see some floating areas, some areas with adhesions. If you take that and perform a biopsy, you will discover that it's endometriosis. Thus, many more endometrioses are present than are being diagnosed.

Concerning your question about non-visible endometriosis, it's true that when a patient presents with pelvic pain and dysmenorrhea, but with no endometriotic lesions visible by laparoscopy, I will nevertheless perform uterosacral resection of both uterosacral ligaments. In 20% of the cases, I will find non-visible endometriosis. But I agree with you that probably in that group, 50% of the patients will come back and say, 'Doctor, I still have pain'. The only thing we can do for these patients is a therapeutic assay. For example, you can try GnRH agonist for 3 months as a therapeutic diagnosis. If she still has pain after 2 or 3 months of GnRH agonist therapy, you can say to the patient, 'It's not related to endometriosis. It's not related to the uterus. I cannot do anything for you.' But if the patient is better after 3 months of GnRH therapy, then before the end of the activity of the GnRH agonist, we will begin administering continuous progestogens. In particular, she will start on progestogens 3 weeks after the last injection of GnRH agonist. This is the only possibility we have at the present time.

Dr. Momoeda: The reason why I ask you that question is I have often wondered about how to treat patients in the pain group, especially in the early stage. We can do nothing by surgery for these patients, so your comment is very helpful.

Professor Donnez: I think that the only possibility that we have is to stop ovarian cyclicity and ovarian secretion. If we put the patient in amenorrhea, we will reduce the secretion of cytokines, or prostaglandin, and we hope that this will have some effect on pelvic pain.

Session 3
Review

Gynecologic and Obstetric Investigation

Gynecol Obstet Invest 2002;54(suppl 1):24–29
DOI: 10.1159/000066291

Laparoscopic Surgery for the Management of Ovarian Endometrioma

Souichi Yoshida Tasuku Harada Tomio Iwabe Naoki Terakawa

Department of Obstetrics and Gynecology, Tottori University School of Medicine, Yonago, Japan

Key Words
Ovarian endometrioma · Laparoscopic surgery · Recurrence · Dysmenorrhea · Infertility · Interleukin-6

Abstract
The purpose of this study was to evaluate the effects of laparoscopic surgery on the symptoms associated with ovarian endometrioma. We also examined serum IL-6 concentrations in patients with endometrioma. Ninety-two patients who underwent laparoscopic surgery for ovarian endometrioma were enrolled in this study. The mean duration of follow-up was 27.6 months. Transvaginal ultrasound examinations revealed a recurrence of endometrioma in 13% of the cases. We evaluated the severity of dysmenorrhea using a 0–3-point verbal rating scale, and found that the dysmenorrhea score was statistically improved after the operation. Follicular growth was preserved in 94%, and the pregnancy rate was 43%. We measured serum IL-6 concentrations in 14 patients with ovarian endometrioma and 4 patients with benign gynecologic disease without endometriosis. IL-6 was significantly higher in patients with endometrioma than in those without endometriosis at the time of diagnosis. The mean serum IL-6 concentration significantly decreased after the operation. In conclusion, laparoscopic surgery is effective for alleviating pain and preserving fertility in patients with endometrioma. Measurements of serum IL-6 concentrations may be useful for the management of endometrioma.

Introduction

Ovarian endometrioma is a common disease lesion among women with endometriosis. It is well known that medical therapy with GnRH analog or Danazol alone is not effective for ovarian endometrioma. Conservative treatments, such as ultrasound guided aspiration and ethanol sclerotherapy, have been proposed [1, 2]. However, these treatments are associated with a relatively high rate of recurrence and adverse effects on the surrounding normal tissues [1, 3]. Thus, management of ovarian endometrioma has been a matter of debate. The purpose of this study was to evaluate the effects of laparoscopic surgery on the symptoms associated with ovarian endometrioma. In addition, we measured serum concentrations of IL-6 before and after laparoscopic surgery.

Materials and Methods

After obtaining informed consent, 92 patients who underwent laparoscopic surgery for ovarian endometrioma during August 1994 to December 2000 in Tottori University Hospital were enrolled in this study. Ovarian endometrioma was diagnosed by means of ultrasound examination and magnetic resonance imaging. Patients' clinical characteristics are shown in table 1. Patients were followed up 2–78 months after the laparoscopic surgery. Laparoscopic cystectomy was performed for 87 patients. Of these patients, 23 cases underwent bilateral cystectomy. Five patients received oophorectomy. Laparoscopic myomectomy (n = 5) and laparoscopically assisted vaginal hysterectomy (LAVH) (n = 6) were also performed with ovarian surgery. At the time of laparoscopic surgery, peritoneal endometriot-

KARGER
Fax + 41 61 306 12 34
E-Mail karger@karger.ch
www.karger.com

0378–7346/02/0545–0024$18.50/0

Accessible online at:
www.karger.com/goi

Souichi Yoshida, MD
Department of Obstetrics and Gynecology
Tottori University School of Medicine
Nishimachi 36-1, Yonago, Tottori, 683-8504 (Japan)
Tel. +81 859 34 8127, Fax +81 859 34 8089, E-Mail souichi@grape.med.tottori-u.ac.jp

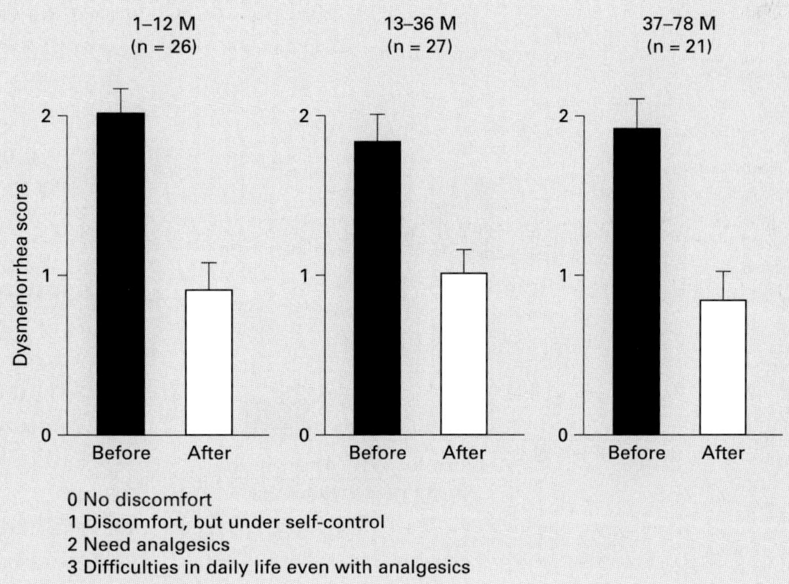

Fig. 1. Dysmenorrhea score before and after laparoscopic surgery. Severity of dysmenorrhea in 74 patients was evaluated before the operation and at the follow-up visit using a 0–3-point verbal rating scale (shown in this figure) to examine whether the laparoscopic surgery improved dysmenorrhea. The mean dysmenorrhea score was statistically improved even in the period of more than 3 years.

Table 1. Clinical characteristics of the patients

Number of cases	92
Age, years	33.0 (13–49)
Cyst size, cm	4.4 (1.5–8.8)
Serum CA 125 (U/ml)	86.8 (0.7–800)
R-ASRM scores	47.6 (4–126)
Follow-up, months	27.6 (2–78)

Table 2. Recurrence of ovarian endometrioma after laparoscopic cystectomy

	Postoperative period, months			Total
	1–12	13–36	37–78	
Total	1/28 (4%)	6/31 (19%)	4/26 (15%)	11/85 (13%)
Patients with residual lesions	1/4 (25%)	0/4 (0%)	2/5 (40%)	3/13 (23%)

ic lesions and residual lesions of ovarian endometrioma were coagulated using an argon plasma coagulator (APC 300, ERBE, Germany).

Transvaginal ultrasonography was performed in order to determine the recurrence of endometrioma in 85 patients who received laparoscopic cystectomy. Patients were divided into three groups according to the postoperative periods, as shown in table 2. Postoperative periods were defined as the duration from surgery to the latest visit to the hospital. We next examined whether the laparoscopic surgery improved dysmenorrhea. Of 92 patients, 74 patients self-evaluated the severity of their dysmenorrhea before the operation and at the follow-up visit using a 0–3-point verbal rating scale (shown in fig. 1). In addition, we examined the presence of follicular growth in the operated ovary and pregnancy after the operation. Follicle monitoring was performed in 34 patients by means of ultrasound examination. Pregnancy rate was determined in 35 patients who expressed a desire to have a child.

We also investigated serum IL-6 levels in patients with endometrioma. Fourteen patients who underwent laparoscopic surgery for ovarian endometrioma during November 1999–October 2000 were included in this study. Four patients without endometriosis who underwent laparoscopic surgery for benign ovarian cyst or myoma uteri served as the study control. None of the patients had inflammatory disease, and informed consent was obtained from all patients. The mean age of patients was 35 years (range: 27–48 years) and the mean diameter of endometrioma was 4.7 cm (range: 2.0–7.8 cm). The average revised American Society of Reproductive Medicine (R-ASRM) score was 57.5 points (range: 24–124). Eight patients had unilateral endometrioma and 6 patients had bilateral cysts. Serum concentrations of IL-6 were measured by means of enzyme-linked immunosorbent assay (ELISA) at the time of diagnosis and two weeks after the laparoscopic cystectomy. We also simultaneously measured serum C-reactive protein (CRP) and CA 125. Samples with elevated CRP were excluded. To compare the values of serum concentrations of IL-6, results were analyzed using Mann-Whitney U test. The data are expressed as means ± SEM. A level of $p < 0.05$ was accepted as indicating statistical significance.

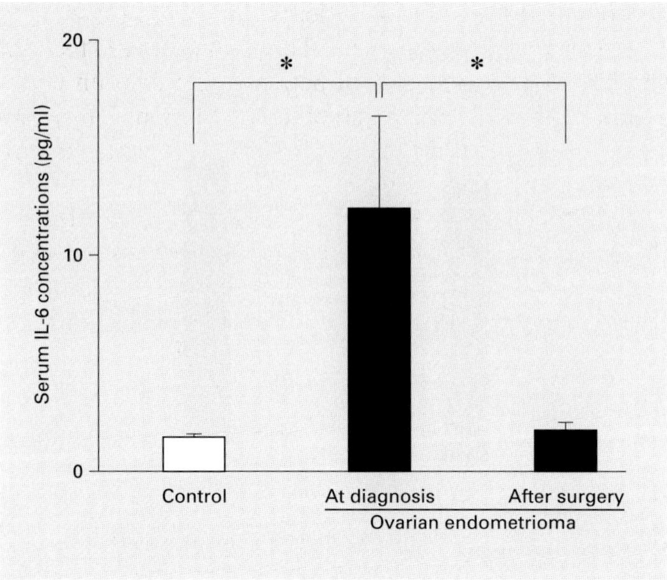

Fig. 2. Serum IL-6 concentrations of 14 patients who underwent laparoscopic surgery for ovarian endometrioma were measured before and after laparoscopic surgery. Four patients without endometriosis who underwent laparoscopic surgery for benign ovarian cyst or myoma uteri served as the study control. Results are given as means ± SEM. Statistical significance of the differences is indicated by * $p < 0.05$.

Results

A recurrence of endometrioma in the treated ovary was detected in one patient in the one-year group, in six patients in the 1–3 year group, and in 4 patients in the group of more than 3 years (table 2). The recurrence rate was 13%. In 13 cases, we could not completely remove the cyst wall, which densely adhered to the rectum. Recurrence was detected in three patients and the recurrence rate was 23% in these cases (table 2).

We next examined whether the laparoscopic surgery improved dysmenorrhea. The mean dysmenorrhea score was statistically improved even in the period of more than 3 years (fig. 1). We also examined the presence of follicular growth and pregnancy after the operation. Follicular growth in the postoperative ovary was observed in 32 cases among 34 patients by means of transvaginal ultrasound follicle monitoring (94%). Pregnancy was achieved in 15 cases among 35 patients (43%).

IL-6 concentrations before laparoscopic surgery were significantly higher in patients with endometrioma than in those without endometriosis (12.2 ± 4.2 vs. 1.39 ± 0.21 pg/ml, $p < 0.05$). We next compared serum IL-6 concentrations of patients with endometrioma before and after laparoscopic surgery. The mean serum IL-6 concentration significantly decreased to 1.83 ± 0.34 pg/ml two weeks after the surgery. The IL-6 levels were similar to those of patients without endometrioma (fig. 2). There were no positive correlations between the serum levels of IL-6 and those of CA 125 (data not shown).

Discussion

Ovarian endometriosis is a common lesion among patients with endometriosis, but the management of endometrioma is still a matter of debate. In the present study, evaluation of disease recurrence in the ovary after laparoscopic surgery revealed a recurrence rate of 13%. We also evaluated the effects of laparoscopic surgery on pain symptoms associated with ovarian endometrioma. Dysmenorrhea was significantly improved even more than three years after the surgery. Follicle monitoring showed the development of a follicle in 94% of the treated ovaries, suggesting that ovarian function was preserved in the surgically treated ovary. Pregnancies were achieved in 43% of patients who desired conception after the operation. In contrast, one study reported a recurrence rate of 31.8% during a mean follow-up period of 20 months after the combined treatment of ultrasound-guided aspiration and medical therapy of ovarian endometrioma [1]. On the other hand, as shown in this study, the recurrence rate of laparoscopic cystectomy was only 13%, even after a longer follow-up period. In addition, unexpected drawbacks were reported. Patients who received ethanol sclerotherapy after ultrasound-guided aspiration of endometrioma reportedly had severe and unusual adhesions surrounding the ovary [3]. A possible toxic effect on the ova of injected ethanol located in the surrounding ovarian cortex has not been completely confirmed. According to these findings, laparoscopic surgery is a safe and effective treatment for alleviation of pain and achievement of pregnancy in patients with endometrioma.

Although measurements of serum concentrations of CA 125 or CA 19-9 support the diagnosis and management of endometrioma, these levels do not always reflect the status of the disease. Recent studies have suggested that cytokines were involved in the pathogenesis of endometriosis and in endometriosis-associated infertility [4, 5]. We previously demonstrated that IL-6 concentrations in peritoneal fluid of patients with endometriosis were significantly higher than in those without endometriosis, and that IL-6 may participate in the pathogenesis of endometriosis [6, 7]. In addition, we indicated that endometriotic stromal cells, as well as peritoneal macrophages, may be another important source of IL-6 in the peritoneal fluid [8]. Therefore, we hypothesized that serum IL-6 concentrations are related to the condition of patients with ovarian endometrioma. To prove this hypothesis, we measured serum IL-6 concentrations in patients with endometrioma. Although serum concentrations of IL-6 did not correlate with those of CA 125, IL-6 concentrations were significantly higher in patients with endometrioma than in those without endometriosis, and decreased to the levels of patients without endometriosis after the laparoscopic surgery. These results indicated that the increased serum IL-6 of patients with ovarian endometrioma may originate in their disease lesion. Thus, IL-6 may become another marker for endometrioma to support diagnosis and evaluate the disease conditions.

In conclusion, laparoscopic surgery is an effective treatment for ovarian endometrioma. Measurements of serum IL-6 concentrations may be useful for the management of endometrioma.

References

1 Mittal S, Kumar S, Kumar A, Verma A: Ultrasound guided aspiration of endometrioma – a new therapeutic modality to improve reproductive outcome. Int J Gynaecol Obstet 1999; 65:17–23.
2 Noma J, Yoshida N: Efficacy of ethanol sclerotherapy for ovarian endometriomas. Int J Gynaecol Obstet 2001;72:35–39.
3 Okagaki R, Osuga Y, Momoeda M, Tsutsumi O, Taketani Y: Laparoscopic findings after ultrasound-guided transvaginal ethanol sclerotherapy for ovarian endometrial cyst. Hum Reprod 1999;14:270.
4 Harada T, Iwabe T, Terakawa N: Role of cytokines in endometriosis. Fertil Steril 2001;76:1–10.
5 Iwabe T, Harada T, Terakawa N: Role of cytokines in endometriosis-associated infertility. Gynecol Obstet Invest 2002;53(suppl 1):19–25.
6 Harada T, Yoshioka H, Yoshida S, Iwabe T, Onohara Y, Tanikawa M, Terakawa N: Increased interleukin-6 levels in peritoneal fluid of infertile patients with active endometriosis. Am J Obstet Gynecol 1997;176:593–597.
7 Yoshioka H, Harada T, Iwabe T, Nagano Y, Taniguchi F, Tanikawa M, Terakawa N: Menstrual cycle-specific inhibition of the proliferation of endometrial stromal cells by interleukin 6 and its soluble receptor. Am J Obstet Gynecol 1999;180:1088–1094.
8 Tsudo T, Harada T, Iwabe T, Tanikawa M, Nagano Y, Ito M, Taniguchi F, Terakawa N: Altered gene expression and secretion of interleukin-6 in stromal cells derived from endometriotic tissues. Fertil Steril 2000;73:205–211.

Post-Presentation Discussion

Professor Hoshiai: Thank you very much, Dr. Yoshida. This paper is now open for discussion.

Professor Donnez: I have two questions. You mentioned that laparoscopic surgery provoked a decrease in IL-6. Have you an idea of the effect of medical therapy without surgery? My second question is: Is there a relationship between the serum level of IL-6 and CA 125?

Dr. Yoshida: I did not show the data, but we also measured serum concentrations before and after the GnRH agonist therapy. The GnRH agonist treatment decreased the serum levels of IL-6, and we isolated endometriotic stromal cells from surgical specimens of ovarian endometrioma with or without GnRH treatment before surgery. The result indicated that treatment with GnRH agonist reduced IL-6 production.

Professor Donnez: This means that the GnRH agonist decreased the activity of the stromal cells, probably by reducing vascularization of the stromal cells.

Dr. Yoshida: Yes, I think you are right. As to your second question, we examined the relationship of IL-6 and CA 125, but we could not detect a positive correlation.

Dr. Maeda: I'd like to ask you one question. It is very interesting that IL-6, which is a monokine, is also produced by the endometriotic tissue, especially active lesions. You demonstrated that TNF-α augmented the level of IL-6 in the endometriotic stromal cells. My question is, what kind of cells in the peritoneal fluid is producing the TNF-α?

Dr. Yoshida: TNF-α is mainly produced by peritoneal macrophages, and maybe the surrounding region of endometriotic disease.

Dr. Suginami: In Japan, it is widely accepted that follow-up of CA 125 levels after treatment is a kind of tool to detect the recurrence of the disease. In your presentation, you noted that IL-6 is also a good tool to detect recurrence after treatment. From the point of view of power of detection, which tool is more effective to detect disease recurrence?

Dr. Yoshida: As you say, CA 125 is useful to detect recurrence, but it did not correlate with the ability of disease lesions to recur, given that CA 125 levels also increased at the time of menstruation and according to various other fluctuations in the status of the patient. Thus, as I showed in my presentation, we think that the sensitivity of IL-6 to detect recurrence is greater than that of CA 125.

Dr. Suginami: Do you have any evidence to support that conclusion?

Dr. Yoshida: We don't have any positive evidence, but we will test for such evidence in the future.

Dr. Harada: I am a co-author of this paper. We did not compare the sensitivity of IL-6 and CA 125. We simply measured the levels before and just after the operation. We do not follow up the levels of IL-6, and so we do not have an answer to your question at the present time. However, as Dr. Yoshida previously mentioned, we thought that IL-6 may reflect the activity of the cells in the ovarian endometrioma. Our hypothesis is that this may relate to the recurrence rate, or to patients who show recurrence in a relatively short period after surgery. Thus, we may differentiate the activity of the cells in the endometriomas. This is one of our hypotheses. We may use these cytokine levels as tools.

Dr. Osuga: When comparing the levels of IL-6 and CA 125, the interesting point of contrast is that IL-6 has various bioactivities as compared to CA 125, and thus the possibility exists that there is a relationship between the symptoms and IL-6 levels. Do you have any idea how the IL-6 levels are reflected by the symptoms related to endometrioma?

Dr. Yoshida: That's a very interesting question, but I don't have any theories.

Professor Donnez: I would like to make one comment. Can you show the slide again with the endoscopic picture? If I can just make a simple, but I believe important, comment on what we can see in this slide with regard to the surgical technique. You see that the ovary is not so big, and the endometrioma can be seen here. You have removed the capsula, but by removing the capsula, you have also removed a part of the normal ovarian cortex. If you had opened only this area, you would not have been obliged to remove this part of the normal ovarian cortex. We need to do everything we can to preserve the quantity of the remaining ovary.

Professor Hoshiai: Thank you very much for your good suggestion. I have one question for you, Professor Donnez, related to this problem. Dr. Yoshida said that after the laparoscopic cystectomy, cases with an absence of ovarian function were just 2%. Is that the same incidence you found?

Professor Donnez: It is lower. There is a difference between normal function, by which I mean a level of follicle stimulating hormone (FSH) on cycles on day three of less than 15, and a normal menstrual cycle. But if you stimulate, you will see a huge difference. I am quite sure that if you try to stimulate an ovary, like the one you can see on the right side of the slide, with recombinant FSH of gonadotrophin, the number of follicles with mature oocytes will be significantly lower than expected. This is because a part of the ovarian cortex has been removed. In a study in *Fertility and Sterility* by Loh et al., it was published that after ovarian cystectomy the ovarian function was apparently normal. However, when they stimulated, they observed a poor response in more than 25% of cases. Thus, we must really be careful about that.

Professor Hoshiai: This means that the lower level of ovarian response is due to removal of the cortex. I think that the root of the problem is the suture technique.

Professor Donnez: The suture technique and coagulation. I say coagulation because, due to the location of the ovaries and the ovarian vessel, when you remove deeply, there is also a risk that coagulation will be needed near the ovarian hilus. When you reach a certain point, you get very close to the emergence of the ovarian vessels, and the bleeding starts at that point. What can you do to stop the bleeding, except coagulate the blood vessel? If you coagulate too deeply, you will also coagulate the ovarian vessels and decrease vascularization to the normal ovarian cortex. I think we really have to take care to preserve ovarian function.

Professor Hoshiai: Another question for Dr. Yoshida is related to a clinical consideration. In the earlier part of your presentation, you classified the recurrence rate according to a complete resection group and a residual lesion group. Following laparoscopic surgery, do you use GnRH agonist or danazol or a similar drug for patients in the residual lesion group?

Dr. Yoshida: We use GnRH agonist for some patients, but not all.

Professor Hoshiai: So, the data you presented included both the medicated and unmedicated patients?

Dr. Yoshida: Yes, both are included.

Dr. Harada: May I ask Professor Donnez a question? You mentioned that the recurrence rate after coagulation of ovarian endometrioma is 6%. This is a surprising figure for me, because the reason we perform cystectomy is in order to reduce the recurrence rate. How do you coagulate or vaporize the inner wall?

Professor Donnez: The recurrence rate I quoted is taken from the study of Gordts and Brosens and from my study, where a recurrence rate of 6–7% was observed after microsurgery by laparotomy. This was 15 years ago. More recently, after laser surgery, recurrence rates of 6% were also reported by our group in 1997 in *Human Reproduction*. In some cases, recurrence was due to the appearance of another endometrial cyst in the same ovary, or in the contralateral ovary. With our technique, the recurrence rate after vaporization is higher for those unfamiliar with the procedure, because they are being tentative. We have to carefully vaporize or coagulate the internal wall of the endometrioma very, very systematically. And we also have to flush with saline solution continuously. You have to be sure to vaporize all of the endometrial tissue, and this is why I said during my presentation that with insufficient surgery there is a risk of recurrence. But it's not recurrence; it's persistence. It's because the surgeon has neglected to vaporize a part of the cyst. For sure, one year later, a cyst will recur from this small neglected part. It is a difficult technique, but it is better for the ovary. One of my colleagues or I will systematically supervise all of the ovarian endometrioma vaporization procedures performed at our institution, even those by a senior resident. We check ourselves systematically in all cases. We find that if we fail to do so, the recurrence rate will be much higher, because the assistant has vaporized too superficially or has neglected a small area. They have sometimes made just a superficial burn, but it is not deep enough.

Dr. Harada: What kind of laser do you use?

Professor Donnez: A CO_2 laser with the swift equipment. As you know, the swift laser, or CO_2 laser, has been used in plastic surgery for resurfacing, and the depth of the vaporization is 100 µm. You have to vaporize just the internal surface of the endometrioma. But I noticed that you have an argon beam laser. Why not use the argon beam to vaporize peritoneal lesions? However, you have to take care to not go too deep, given that the penetration of the argon beam laser can be greater than 100 µm. You don't want to induce thermal damage to the ovarian cortex. But you can achieve exactly the same result with the argon beam laser.

Dr. Harada: We will try it and compare.

Session 3
Review

Gynecologic and Obstetric Investigation

Gynecol Obstet Invest 2002;54(suppl 1):30–35
DOI: 10.1159/000066292

Laparoscopic Treatment of Endometrioma-Associated Infertility and Pregnancy Outcome

Naoyuki Takuma Kazuo Sengoku Bochen Pan Keiko Wada Tomofumi Yamauchi Toshinobu Miyamoto Daisuke Ohsumi Mutsuo Ishikawa

Department of Obstetrics and Gynecology, Asahikawa Medical College, Asahikawa, Japan

Key Words
Endometrioma · Infertility · Laparoscopy · IVF-ET · Cystectomy · Ethanol fixation · Fenestration

Abstract
Ovarian endometriomas do not respond well to medical treatment with hormonal suppression, and surgical removal of the endometriomas is usually required. In this study, we attempt to identify the optimal laparoscopic procedures in laparoscopic treatment of ovarian-endometrioma-associated infertility. Among cases in which patients received no IVF-ET after the laparoscopic treatment, the pregnancy rate after complete cystectomy of endometriomas was statistically lower than that after fenestration with electrocoagulation of the cyst wall. Among cases in which patients received IVF-ET, there was no difference in ovarian response between patients that had complete cystectomy and fenestration with electrocoagulation of the cyst wall. However, the pregnancy rate in patients who had aspiration alone was statistically lower than that in patients who had aspiration followed by ethanol fixation. Thus, it appears that for patients who do not require follow-up IVF-ET, fenestration with electrocoagulation of the cyst wall is suitable, whereas for patients who need follow-up IVF-ET, ethanol fixation may be a better choice.

Introduction

Endometriosis is a common finding in women suffering from female infertility [1]. Moreover, ovarian endometriomas do not respond well to medical treatment with hormonal suppression [2–4], and surgical removal of the endometriomas is usually required. In general, laparoscopic surgery has been considered the method of choice for the treatment of ovarian endometriomas. However, controversy remains regarding which laparoscopic approach is the best for the treatment of endometrioma [5–9]. Some surgeons prefer performing a complete cystectomy, i.e., stripping the cyst wall off the ovary, because of the concern of an associated clear-cell carcinoma [10, 11]. On the other hand, the ovarian follicular response of postcystectomy ovaries has to be considered for the infertile women. In this regard, Beretta et al. [12] reported that the 24-month cumulative pregnancy rate was higher in the group treated with laparoscopic cystectomy than in the group treated with drainage of the endometrioma and coagulation of the inner lining. A recent clinical study also showed that postcystectomy ovaries could produce a comparable number of follicles as normal ovaries when stimulated with gonadotropins [13]. In contrast, Hemmings et al. [14] suggested that ovarian cystectomy in cases of endometriomas could be deleterious for residual normal ovarian cortex. Moreover, Donnez et al. [15] proposed a

KARGER
Fax + 41 61 306 12 34
E-Mail karger@karger.ch
www.karger.com

Accessible online at:
www.karger.com/goi

Naoyuki Takuma, MD, PhD
Department of Obstetrics and Gynecology, Asahikawa Medical College
Midorigaoka higashi 2-1-1-1
Asahikawa, Hokkaido, 078-8510 (Japan)
Tel. +81 166 68 2562, Fax +81 166 68 2569, E-Mail ntakuma@asahikawa-med.ac.jp

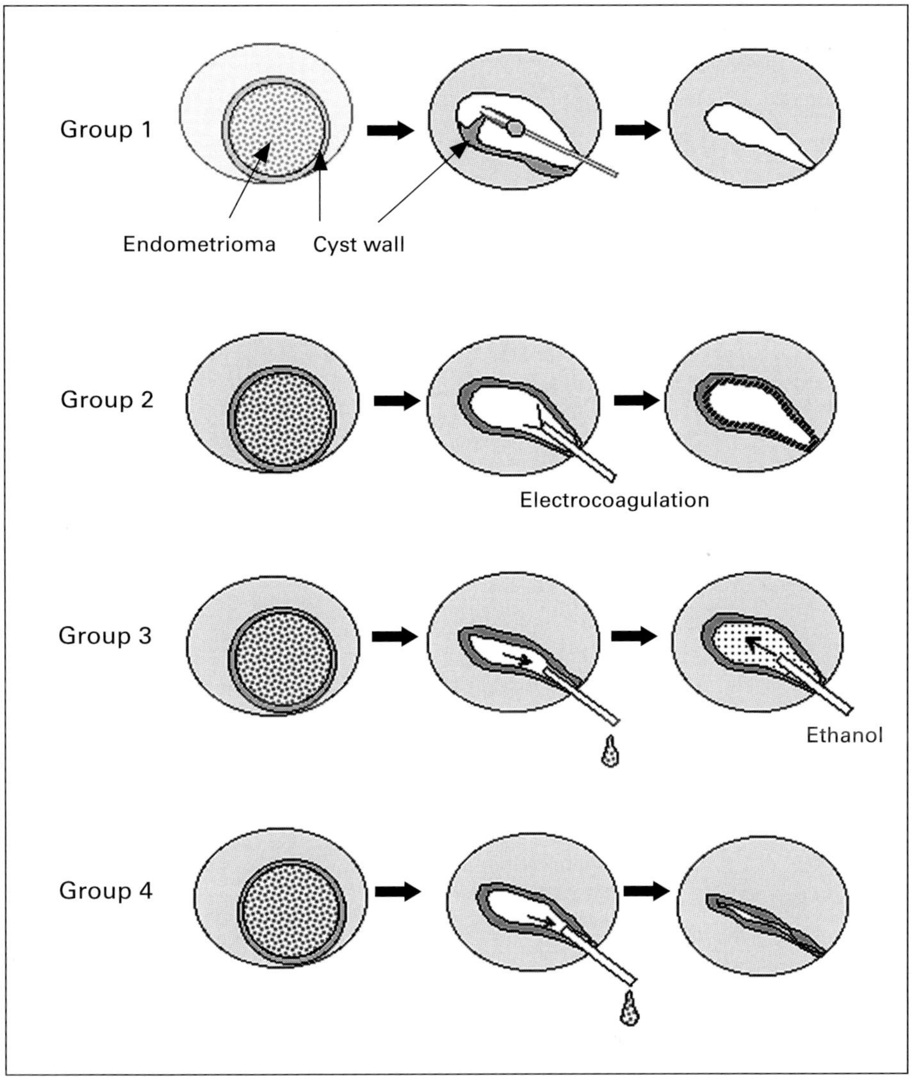

Fig. 1. The schema of the four laparoscopic procedures in Asahikawa Medical College is shown in figure 1. Group 1: Laparoscopic ovarian cystectomy, stripping the cyst wall off the ovary. Group 2: Laparoscopic ovarian fenestration with electrocoagulation of the cyst wall. Group 3: Laparoscopic aspiration of ovarian endometriomas followed by ethanol fixation. Group 4: Laparoscopic aspiration of ovarian endometriomas alone. Please note that the 100% ethanol must be retained to fix the cyst wall in the cyst for 15 min (group 3).

laparoscopic vaporization technique as a better alternative preserving the normal residual ovarian cortex. In this study, we retrospectively analyzed 243 cases of endometrioma-associated infertility with an emphasis on the laparoscopic surgical modalities and their postoperative pregnancy rate. Our purpose was to identify the optimal laparoscopic procedure for the treatment of ovarian-endometriomas associated infertility.

Material and Methods

From January 1989 to December 1998, diagnostic and surgical laparoscopy was performed for 732 infertile patients in Asahikawa Medical College Hospital. Among these cases, ovarian endometriomas were found in 243 patients. Patients with ovarian endometriomas were treated with one of the following four therapeutic modalities according to the surgeon's preference (fig. 1). Group 1 consisted of 98 patients who underwent laparoscopic ovarian cystectomy, including stripping the cyst wall off the ovary; group 2 consisted of 66 patients who underwent laparoscopic ovarian fenestration with electrocoagulation of the cyst wall; group 3 consisted of 25 patients who underwent laparoscopic aspiration of ovarian endometriomas followed by ethanol fixation; group 4 consisted of 54 patients who underwent laparoscopic aspiration of ovarian endometriomas alone (table 1). In all cases, we routinely performed adhesiolysis of fallopian tubes, and electrocoagulation of pelvic endometriotic lesions. Patients were followed up at 24 months (median follow-up interval, 12 months) after the operation without medical treatment with hormonal suppression. In cases of bilateral tubal obstruction or if a pregnancy was not achieved within one year from the laparoscopic operation, IVF-ET was recommended, and it was performed as described [16]. Patients who underwent IVF-ET were followed up at 36 months after laparoscopic surgery (median follow-up interval, 20 months),

Table 1. Characteristics of patients with endometrioma

	Group 1	Group 2	Group 3	Group 4
Patients	98	66	25	54
Age, years	31.2 ± 3.5	30.7 ± 3.7	31.5 ± 4.0	31.0 ± 3.3
Diameter of endometrioma, cm	4.2 ± 2.0	3.8 ± 1.6	4.1 ± 1.9	3.5 ± 1.4

Values given as means ± SD. All p values >0.05 (Welch's t test).

Table 2. Pregnancy outcome at 24 months after laparoscopic surgery in no IVF-ET cases

	Group 1	Group 2	Group 3	Group 4	Total
Patients	62	49	15	38	164
Pregnancies	16	24	5	13	58
Pregnancy rate, %	25.8[a]	49.0[a]	33.3	26.3	41.0

[a] $p = 0.011$; $p < 0.05$ (χ^2 test).

Table 3. IVF-ET outcome at 36 months after laparoscopic surgery

	Group 1	Group 2	Group 3	Group 4	Total
Patients	36	17	10	16	79
IVF cycles	69	39	31	43	182
Retrieved oocytes (mean ± SD)[a]	7.3 ± 4.9	8.0 ± 4.3	8.8 ± 4.6	8.8 ± 5.4	8.1 ± 4.9
Pregnancies	18	6	7	4	35
Pregnancy rate, %	50.0	35.3	70.0[b]	25.0[b]	44.3

[a] Not statistically significant; All p values >0.05 (Welch's t test).
[b] $p = 0.032$; $p < 0.05$ (Fisher's exact probability test).

and the results of the IVF-ET including number of cycles, number of retrieved oocytes and the cumulative pregnancy rate were determined.

Statistical Analysis

Welch's t test, χ^2 test and Fisher's exact probability test were performed where appropriate.

Results

There were no statistically significant differences between groups in mean age or endometrioma size (average of three diameters) (table 1).

We first studied the cases in which the patients received no IVF-ET after the laparoscopy (table 2). Pregnancy was achieved in 41.0% of all cases. Group 2 had the highest cumulative pregnancy rate, followed in order by groups 3, 4, and 1 (49.0, 33.3, 26.3, 25.8%, respectively). The difference in pregnancy rate between groups 2 and 1 was statistically significant (25.8 versus 49.0%, $p < 0.05$).

Then, we analyzed the 36-month cumulative pregnancy rate among cases in which patients underwent IVF-ET after the laparoscopy (table 3). No difference was found between each group in the number of IVF cycles and the retrieved oocytes. The total pregnancy rate at 36 months after the laparoscopic surgery in all groups was 44.3%. The pregnancy rate in group 3 was statistically higher than that in group 4 (70.0 versus 25.0%, $p < 0.05$). However, there was no statistically significant difference between groups 1 and 2 in the pregnancy rate (50.0 versus 35.3%).

Discussion

In patients who did not undergo IVF-ET after the laparoscopic treatment, the pregnancy rate after complete cystectomy of endometriomas was statistically lower than that after fenestration with electrocoagulation of the cyst wall. Our finding supports those reported by Hemmings et al. showing that fenestration and coagulation were superior to cystectomy [14]. The lower pregnancy rate might be attributable to ovarian damage caused by endometrioma stripping. Donnez et al. suggested that stripping of endometrioma resulted in loss of viable cortex during surgery [17]. These authors also demonstrated that stripping of endometrioma caused bleeding at the hilus and subsequent requirement of extensive coagulation [1, 17].

On the other hand, our results are different from those reported by Beretta et al. [12]. These authors reported that, after fenestration and coagulation, not only was the pregnancy rate lower, but the recurrence rate was also higher than that after cystectomy. Although we could not identify a clear explanation for the discrepancy, it is possible that the reported lower pregnancy rates after fenestration and coagulation could be due to rapid recurrence. It has been reported that fenestration of the endometrioma alone is ineffective, and rapid recurrence occurs [18, 19]. Thus, if the cyst wall lining was coagulated insufficiently or non-treated areas remained, rapid recurrence of endometrioma could occur.

A recent study reported that the specimens obtained using the stripping technique for ovarian endometrioma did not show the morphologic characteristics seen in normal ovarian tissue [20]. However, the function of the remaining ovarian tissue is still a question. In almost all cases of the stripping technique for ovarian endometrioma, electrocoagulation is required for hemostasis in the remaining ovarian tissue. This may cause damage to the tissue and hamper the ovarian function.

In patients who received IVF-ET after the laparoscopic surgery, we did not find a difference between each group in ovarian response. For patients who underwent IVF-ET in our hospital, gonadotropins were used for superovulation before oocyte retrieval [16]. Loh et al. [13] demonstrated that the postcystectomy ovary, when stimulated with gonadotropins, was able to respond comparably with the normal ovary. Donnez et al. [15] also suggested that cyst wall vaporization allowed preservation of a good ovarian response to stimulation by gonadotropins. Thus, ovarian response to stimulation by gonadotropins was not reduced by either laparoscopic procedure. Our results also support those in case-control studies reported by these authors.

Some investigators have reported a reduction in oocyte quality because ovarian endometriomas produce substances that are toxic to maturing oocytes [21–23]. However, Donnez et al. [15] suggested that the lower fertilization rate seen in patients with endometrioma could be corrected by surgery. In our study, the pregnancy rate of the aspiration alone technique was statistically lower than that of aspiration followed by ethanol fixation. Aspiration of the endometioma alone was associated with a rapid recurrence [18, 19]. Oocyte quality is likely impaired by the presence of endometrioma in ovaries. It also suggests that oocyte quality can be corrected by removing the endometrioma [15]. Aspiration of ovarian endometriomas followed by ethanol fixation can be performed under vaginal ultrasonography. Thus, if endometrioma recurrence occurs, ethanol fixation under vaginal ultrasonography may be a good treatment.

Conclusions

We conclude that laparoscopic fenestration with coagulation of the cyst wall is associated with a higher pregnancy rate than that of complete cystectomy. Thus, we suggest that the optimal laparoscopic procedure for treatment of ovarian-endometrioma-associated infertility is ovarian fenestration with coagulation of the cyst wall. In cases with follow-up IVF-ET, we could not identify the optimal laparoscopic procedure. However, our results raise the possibility that ethanol fixation may be considered as a first choice in these cases, but further studies are needed.

References

1 Nisolle M, Donnez J: Peritoneal endometriosis, ovarian endometriosis, and adenomyotic nodules of the rectovaginal septum are three different entities. Fertil Steril 1997;68:585–596.

2 Shaw RW: The role of GnRH analogues in the treatment of endometriosis. Br J Obstet Gynaecol 1992;99(suppl 7):9–12.

3 Shaw RW: Treatment of endometriosis. Lancet 1992;340:1267–1271.

4 Rana N, Thomas S, Rotman C, Dmowski WP: Decrease in the size of ovarian endometriomas during ovarian suppression in stage IV endometriosis. Role of preoperative medical treatment. J Reprod Med 1996;41:384–392.

5 Martin DC: Laparoscopic treatment of ovarian endometriomas. Clin Obstet Gynecol 1991;34:452–459.

6 Fayez JA, Vogel MF: Comparison of different treatment methods of endometriomas by laparoscopy. Obstet Gynecol 1991;78:660–665.

7 Crosignani PG, Vercellini P: Conservative surgery for severe endometriosis: Should laparotomy be abandoned definitively? Hum Reprod 1995;10:2412–2418.

8 Crosignani PG, Vercellini P, Biffignandi F, Costantini W, Cortesi I, Imparato E: Laparoscopy versus laparotomy in conservative surgical treatment for severe endometriosis. Fertil Steril 1996;66:706–711.

9 Garry R: Laparoscopic excision of endometriosis: the treatment of choice? Br J Obstet Gynaecol 1997;104:513–515.

10 Fukunaga M, Nomura K, Ishikawa E, Ushigome S: Ovarian atypical endometriosis: its close association with malignant epithelial tumours. Histopathology 1997;30:249–255.

11 Jiang X, Morland SJ, Hitchcock A, Thomas EJ, Campbell IG: Allelotyping of endometriosis with adjacent ovarian carcinoma reveals evidence of a common lineage. Cancer Res 1998; 58:1707–1712.

12 Beretta P, Franchi M, Ghezzi F, Busacca M, Zupi E, Bolis P: Randomized clinical trial of two laparoscopic treatments of endometriomas: cystectomy versus drainage and coagulation. Fertil Steril 1998;70:1176–1180.

13 Loh FH, Tan AT, Kumar J, Ng SC: Ovarian response after laparoscopic ovarian cystectomy for endometriotic cysts in 132 monitored cycles. Fertil Steril 1999;72:316–321.

14 Hemmings R, Bissonnette F, Bouzayen R: Results of laparoscopic treatments of ovarian endometriomas: laparoscopic ovarian fenestration and coagulation. Fertil Steril 1998;70:527–529.

15 Donnez J, Wyns C, Nisolle M: Does ovarian surgery for endometriomas impair the ovarian response to gonadotropin? Fertil Steril 2001; 76:662–665.

16 Sengoku K, Tamate K, Takaoka Y, Morishita N, Ishikawa M: A randomized prospective study of gonadotrophin with or without gonadotrophin-releasing hormone agonist for treatment of unexplained infertility. Hum Reprod 1994;9:1043–1047.

17 Donnez J, Nisolle M, Gillet N, Smets M, Bassil S, Casanas-Roux F: Large ovarian endometriomas. Hum Reprod 1996;11:641–646.

18 Donnez J, Nisolle M, Gillerot S, Anaf V, Clerckx-Braun F, Casanas-Roux F: Ovarian endometrial cysts: The role of gonadotropin-releasing hormone agonist and/or drainage. Fertil Steril 1994;62:63–66.

19 Saleh A, Tulandi T: Reoperation after laparoscopic treatment of ovarian endometriomas by excision and by fenestration. Fertil Steril 1999; 72:322–324.

20 Muzii L, Bianchi A, Croce C, Manci N, Panici PB: Laparoscopic excision of ovarian cysts: is the stripping technique a tissue-sparing procedure? Fertil Steril 2002;77:609–614.

21 Simon C, Gutierrez A, Vidal A, de los Santos MJ, Tarin JJ, Remohi J, Pellicer A: Outcome of patients with endometriosis in assisted reproduction: Results from in-vitro fertilization and oocyte donation. Hum Reprod 1994;9:725–729.

22 Pal L, Shifren JL, Isaacson KB, Chang Y, Leykin L, Toth TL: Impact of varying stages of endometriosis on the outcome of in vitro fertilization-embryo transfer. J Assist Reprod Genet 1998;15:27–31.

23 Yanushpolsky EH, Best CL, Jackson KV, Clarke RN, Barbieri RL, Hornstein MD: Effects of endometriomas on ooccyte quality, embryo quality, and pregnancy rates in in vitro fertilization cycles: A prospective, case-controlled study. J Assist Reprod Genet 1998;15:193–197.

Post-Presentation Discussion

Professor Hoshiai: Thank you very much for your presentation, Dr. Takuma. This paper is now open for discussion.

Dr. Suginami: Dr. Takuma, I would like to make a comment about the treatment of the patient and the process of trying to identify the culprit of infertility. I think there are only a limited number of cases involving patients with only ovarian endometriosis, and likely most patients simultaneously have peritoneal lesions as well. Currently, you treat both peritoneal lesions and ovarian lesions. You are trying to identify the culprit of infertility by analyzing your data. How do you point to a certain factor, and say this is the culprit responsible for the infertility?

Dr. Takuma: Your question is very difficult. In our department, the purpose of laparoscopy is mostly diagnostic, because our goal is to achieve pregnancy for infertile women. Even if we successfully treat endometriosis, we have not necessarily achieved the main goal of our treatment. We could not identify the culprit of infertility using our data.

Professor Donnez: I have three major concerns. My first concern is that when you analyze the pregnancy rate after reproductive technology, the pregnancy rate is given per patient. I do not believe that this is the correct approach, because it is not revealing the actual number of attempts. If you make ten attempts to achieve one pregnancy in one patient, according to your evaluation, the success rate is 100%, whereas per cycle, it's only 10%. This is a huge study, but I believe you can do better with the data. You can evaluate the pregnancy rate per cycle, and I'm sure you will observe some differences.

My second comment is related to your finding, where you say that in 29% of cases after surgery, the patient became pregnant. This value is not similar to the pregnancy rate achieved in most other institutions, which is more than 50%. Your conclusion is right. Likely you have to improve the quality of the surgery. You have to classify patients with pure endometriosis as a cause of infertility. In your group of patients, mixed male and female infertility cases are probably included. Thus, you need to take care in making any conclusion.

My last comment is that I don't really understand what you mean by incomplete removal of red lesions. Does it mean that you have seen red and very active lesions, and that you have decided to destroy some of the lesions but not others? What does this mean exactly?

Dr. Takuma: We tried to remove all visible red lesions.

Professor Donnez: How do you know that there are still non-visible red lesions?

Dr. Takuma: I am not sure about the non-visible lesions.

Professor Donnez: This is the reason why I don't understand what you mean by incomplete removal of red lesions. The comment I am making is very important, because according to your table, you are suggesting that by incomplete removal of red lesions, you are able to achieve the best pregnancy rate. In my opinion, there is a contradiction there.

Dr. Takuma: Yes, but in many cases we cannot coagulate all of the red lesions. If there is a very wide area of red lesions, we cannot coagulate them all.

Professor Donnez: Why not?

Dr. Takuma: In some cases, red lesions are located near the uterine artery and ureter. We could not completely coagulate in those cases. Thus, laparoscopic coagulation is risky in some cases.

Professor Donnez: I don't think that there is a risk. In the group of patients for which you have judged for yourself that the treatment by surgery was incomplete, do you prescribe GnRH agonist afterwards?

Dr. Takuma: Usually we don't use GnRH agonist after laparoscopy.

Professor Donnez: Even if you leave behind red lesions?

Dr. Takuma: Yes, we think that infertility treatment takes precedence over treatment of red lesions. However, we sometimes try a second look operation for observation of the pelvis.

Professor Hoshiai: Thank you, Professor Donnez, for the very helpful comment. Dr. Takuma has a large number of cases, and he can now analyze the data according to your suggestion, and hopefully he will be able to publish the results.

Professor Donnez: It's a large study, and my comment was made in a prospective way. I am sure he can obtain much more scientific data and probably the conclusion of this paper will change. Likely it will have to be submitted later. It will be a lot of work.

Session 3
Original Article

Gynecologic and Obstetric Investigation

Gynecol Obstet Invest 2002;54(suppl 1):36–42
DOI: 10.1159/000066293

Pretreatment for Ovarian Endometrial Cyst before in vitro Fertilization

Nobuhiko Suganuma[a] Yasunori Wakahara[a] Daisuke Ishida[a] Miyuki Asano[a] Takeshi Kitagawa[a] Yoshinori Katsumata[b] Takayuki Moriwaki[b] Madoka Furuhashi[c]

[a]Infertility Center, Toyohashi Municipal Hospital, Toyohashi, [b]Infertility Center, Toyota Memorial Hospital, Toyota, and [c]Department of Obstetrics and Gynecology, The Japanese Red Cross Nagoya First Hospital, Nagoya, Japan

Key Words
Ovarian endometrial cyst · Cyst aspiration · Cystectomy · IVF-ET · Oocyte quality · Fertilization rate

Abstract
Assisted reproductive technology is a widely accepted treatment for infertile women with endometriosis. The presence of an ovarian endometrial cyst reduces the quality of oocytes, while surgical resection of endometrioma may reduce the ovarian reserve for ovarian stimulation by exogenous gonadotropins. To determine what pretreatment should be performed for ovarian endometrial cyst before IVF-ET, we analyzed IVF outcomes with or without pretreatment in patients with endometrioma. Infertile women with endometrioma who underwent IVF-ET were divided into 3 groups, including patients who had received laparotomy or laparoscopy, patients for whom the endometrioma content had been aspirated and treated with or without alcohol fixation, and patients who did not undergo pretreatment. The number of retrieved oocytes, rate of mature oocytes, and fertilization rate were compared among groups. The results showed that pretreatment for endometrioma reduces the number of retrieved oocytes. Although oocyte quality as a rate of mature oocytes was not affected by the presence of an ovarian endometrial cyst, the fertilization rate was improved by cyst aspiration. We propose that surgical pretreatment is not necessary for ovarian endometrial cyst before IVF-ET, but cyst aspiration may be beneficial after several failed attempts of IVF.

Introduction

Assisted reproductive technology (ART) has undergone rapid development recently and has been applied clinically for the treatment of infertile patients. Treatment using in vitro fertilization and embryo transfer (IVF-ET) was first used successfully in England in 1978. The technique quickly spread throughout the world, and has been used in the treatment of infertile couples. In Japan, the first test-tube-baby was born in 1983. Since then, the number of clinics performing IVF has increased rapidly. In 1988, there were 54 clinics nationwide performing IVF, and 1,700 cycles of oocyte-retrieval were performed per year, whereas the respective numbers in 1999 were 471 and 56,299 [1]. About 12,000 IVF babies were born this year. Based on the figure of 1,100,000 babies being delivered in Japan in 1999, more than 1% of newborns were conceived using ART. Thus, IVF-ET has been established as a therapeutic clinical procedure for infertility.

KARGER
Fax + 41 61 306 12 34
E-Mail karger@karger.ch
www.karger.com

0378–7346/02/0545–0036$18.50/0

Accessible online at:
www.karger.com/goi

Nobuhiko Suganuma, MD, PhD
Director, Infertility Center
Toyohashi Municipal Hospital
50 Hakken-nishi, Aotake-cho, Toyohashi 441-8570 (Japan)
Tel. +81 532 33 6111, Fax +81 532 33 6177, E-Mail sugasan@par.odn.ne.jp

Table 1. IVF-ET outcomes in patients with endometriosis or tubal factor

	Endometriosis	Tubal factor
Patients	277	601
Patient age, years	34.0±0.8	33.0±0.9
Duration of infertility, years	6.1±0.7	5.8±0.7
Stimulation cycles	551	1,191
Retrieval cycles	538	1,179
Fertilization rate	54.0% (1,655/3,062)	61.3% (4,603/7,509)
Cleavage rate	91.2% (1,510/1,655)	95.1% (4,379/4,603)
ET cycles	449	999
Implantation rate	11.9% (11/991)	11.0% (281/2,545)
Pregnancy rate	22.3% (100/449)	24.5% (245/999)
Abortion rate	23.0% (23/100)	28.6% (70/245)

Reproduced with the kind permission of Suganuma et al. and the EMART Group, 1992–1994 [3].

The first indication for IVF-ET was tubal factor infertility, given that IVF-ET involves induction of conception omitting the Fallopian tubes. Oocytes are retrieved directly from mature follicles before ovulation, and insemination is performed in the laboratory in vitro. Fertilized oocytes are cultured and the subsequent embryos are transferred into the uterine cavity using an ET tube. Thus, patients whose Fallopian tubes are obstructed can conceive via the IVF-ET technique. However, since IVF also makes it possible to observe the gametes and the fertilization process under a microscope, other infertile factors that may cause fertilization failures have also been indicated.

Endometriosis is one of the most enigmatic gynecological diseases. An association between endometriosis and infertility has been noted. Frequently quoted figures regarding this association are that 25–50% of women with infertility have some degree of endometriosis and that in women proven to have endometriosis, 30–50% will be rendered infertile by the condition. However, the mechanism of infertility associated with endometriosis without obvious pelvic adhesion is poorly understood. Although many possibilities have been investigated [2], no complete consensus has been reached yet.

IVF-ET Outcomes in Patients with Endometriosis

Endometriosis, which is thought to cause problems with oocyte pick-up or transportation of the fertilized oocyte to the uterine cavity, has also been indicated for IVF. Although tubal factor infertility is the most common indication for IVF, the IVF indications for endometriosis are gradually increasing in Japan. In 1989, the ratio was less than 10% of all IVF-ET treatment, but this reached 25% in 1992.

How successful is IVF-ET in patients with endometriosis? To analyze this point, a collaboration of ten university hospitals in Akita, Yamagata, Gunma, Tokyo, Nagoya, Kyoto, Kinki, Tokushima, Fukuoka, and Kumamoto (EMART group) was performed and the results were presented at a symposium during the Fifth World Congress on Endometriosis held in 1996 [3]. By comparison with tubal-factor infertility, IVF outcomes, such as fertilization rate, cleavage rate, and pregnancy rate in patients with endometriosis were somewhat lower, although not significantly different (table 1). Although IVF-ET is a useful tool for the treatment of infertile patients with endometriosis, pregnancy and take-home baby rates are not satisfactory.

Thus, improvements need to be made to this technology to ensure a successful rate for patients with endometriosis on IVF-ET.

Effects of Pretreatment for Ovarian Endometrioma on IVF Outcomes

ART is a widely accepted treatment for infertile women with endometriosis. However, several retrospective analyses of IVF programs, performed to gain clinical knowledge of the factors implicated in the etiology of endometriosis-associated infertility, have demonstrated that the quality of the oocyte and/or embryo is affected in

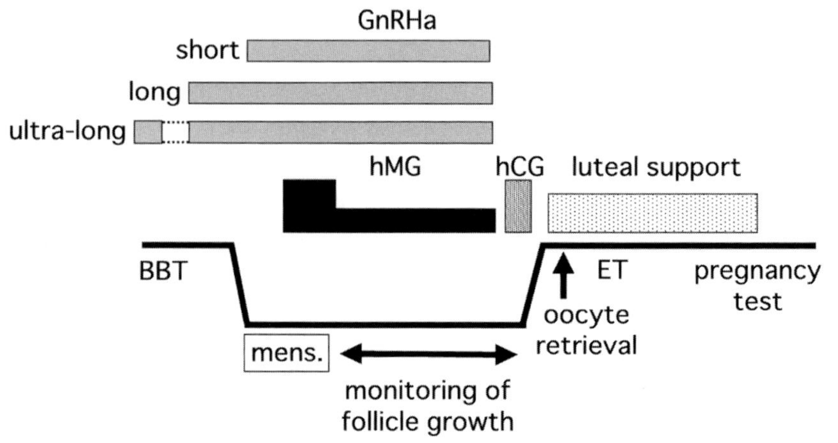

Fig. 1. IVF protocol. GnRHa were administered in short, long, or ultralong protocols [5]. Ovarian hyperstimulation with hMG, monitoring of follicle growth, hCG injection, oocyte retrieval, insemination, ICSI procedures, ET, and luteal support were performed as described elsewhere [6].

Table 2. Profiles of patients pretreated for ovarian endometrial cyst before IVF

	Patients	IVF	ICSI	Age at IVF years	Duration from pretreatment to IVF, ms
Surgery	36	62	25	32.2 ± 3.5	31.2 ± 27.4
Cyst aspirated	23	35	18	33.0 ± 3.8	11.1 ± 12.1
No treatment	20	30	18	32.4 ± 2.8	–

patients with endometriosis and/or ovarian endometrial cyst [4]. In contrast, surgical resection of endometrioma may reduce the ovarian reserve for ovarian stimulation by exogenous gonadotropins. Here, we analyzed IVF outcomes with or without pretreatment in patients with ovarian endometrial cysts.

Infertile women with ovarian endometrial cysts who underwent IVF-ET were divided into 3 groups as follows (table 2); (1) 62 IVF cycles in 36 patients who underwent laparotomy or laparoscopy ('Surgery'group), (2) 35 cycles in 23 patients for whom the endometrioma content was aspirated under transvaginal ultrasonic imaging and treated with or without alcohol fixation ('Cyst aspirated' group), and (3) 30 cycles in 20 patients who did not undergo pretreatment and confirmed ovarian endometriosis at oocyte retrieval ('No treatment' group). Number of intracytoplasmic sperm injection (ICSI) performed, age at IVF, and duration from pretreatment to IVF are summarized in table 2.

Ovarian hyperstimulation using human menopausal gonadotropin (hMG) with gonadotropin-releasing hormone analogs (GnRHa) was performed following a short, long or ultralong protocol as previously described [5] (fig. 1). Injection of human chorionic gonadotropin (hCG), oocyte retrieval, insemination, ICSI, and luteal support were performed as described elsewhere [6].

The number of retrieved oocytes and the numbers and rates of mature oocytes, fertilization and pregnancy in each group are indicated in table 3. These results suggest that pretreatment for ovarian endometrial cyst reduces the number of retrieved oocytes (fig. 2). Although oocyte quality as a rate of mature oocytes was not affected by the presence of endometrioma, fertilization rate was improved by cyst aspiration.

What Pretreatment Should Be Performed for Endometrioma?

It has been proposed that the presence of ovarian endometrial cysts during exogenous hMG stimulation might impair folliculogenesis and oocyte quality, whereas aspi-

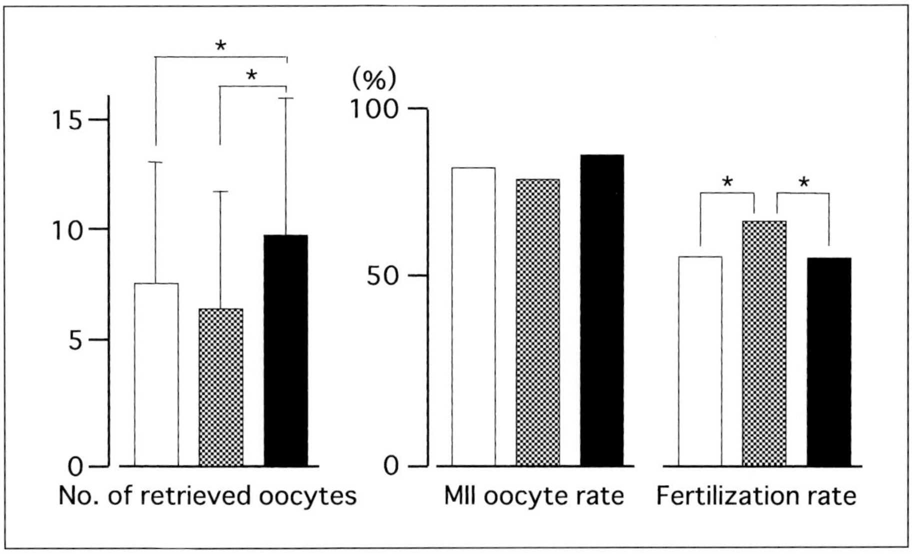

Fig. 2. Numbers of retrieved oocytes, mature oocyte rates, and fertilization rates in patients with ovarian endometrial cysts treated by IVF-ET. *Open*, *dotted* and *solid bars* represent 'Surgery', 'Cyst aspirated' and 'No treatment' groups, respectively, from the data indicated on table 3. * $p < 0.05$.

Table 3. IVF outcomes in patients with ovarian endometrial cyst

	Surgery	Cyst aspirated	No treatment
Retrieved oocytes	7.2 ± 6.2	6.6 ± 5.5	9.7 ± 6.7
MII oocytes	5.7 ± 4.8	5.1 ± 3.7	8.0 ± 5.4
MII oocyte rate	79.1%	77.5%	81.9%
Fertilized oocytes	4.1 ± 3.6	4.5 ± 2.7	5.5 ± 4.9
Fertilization rate	56.8%	67.4%	56.5%
Pregnancies	18	11	11
Pregnancy rate/retrieval	29.0%	31.4%	36.6%

ration of the endometrioma at the time of retrieval may also be detrimental and decrease the chances of pregnancy. Dlugi et al. [7] indicated that women with ovarian endometrial cysts were found to have significantly fewer preovulatory follicles, lower fertilization rates, and fewer embryos transferred compared with patients with tubal factor infertility in a retrospective case-controlled study. In contrast, Olivennes et al. [8] reported that no significant differences in the above parameters were observed when patients with ovarian endometrial cysts were compared with patients having other stages of endometriosis.

Women with endometriomas reportedly had fewer oocytes retrieved, fewer embryos reaching the 4-cell stage and a higher early pregnancy loss rate compared with controls who had no ovarian cysts at the time of retrieval [9]. In contrast, Isaacs et al. [10] noted no difference in number of oocytes, embryos, and pregnancy rates in patients with endometriosis with or without endometriomas. It is important to demonstrate the effect of aspiration before IVF because the current literature suggests a detrimental effect of pelvic endometriosis and endometriomas on follicular development [11].

Surgical treatment of all stages of endometriosis has been shown to enhance overall pregnancy rates [12, 13]. However, surgical treatment before IVF has not been shown to improve pregnancy outcome [8]. Pagidas et al. [14] evaluated the efficacy of repeat operation for endometriosis versus IVF. They concluded that if initial surgery failed to restore fertility in patients with moderate to severe endometriosis, IVF is an effective alternative.

Thus, what pretreatment should be performed for infertile patients having ovarian endometrial cyst before IVF-ET? There are limited data available to enable us to estimate the effect of surgical treatment in addition to ART on the outcome of pregnancy in endometriosis-associated infertility. In addition, there is no randomized controlled study comparing IVF success with or without aspiration or surgical excision of ovarian endometriomas.

Through our present study, we will propose a treatment chart for infertile patients with ovarian endometrial cyst (fig. 3). For the women with severe endometriosis having pelvic pain and dysmenorrhea, laparoscopic surgery including evaporation of peritoneal superficial endometriosis, excision of deep endometriosis, adhesiolysis, and chromotubation may be applied. Even at this time,

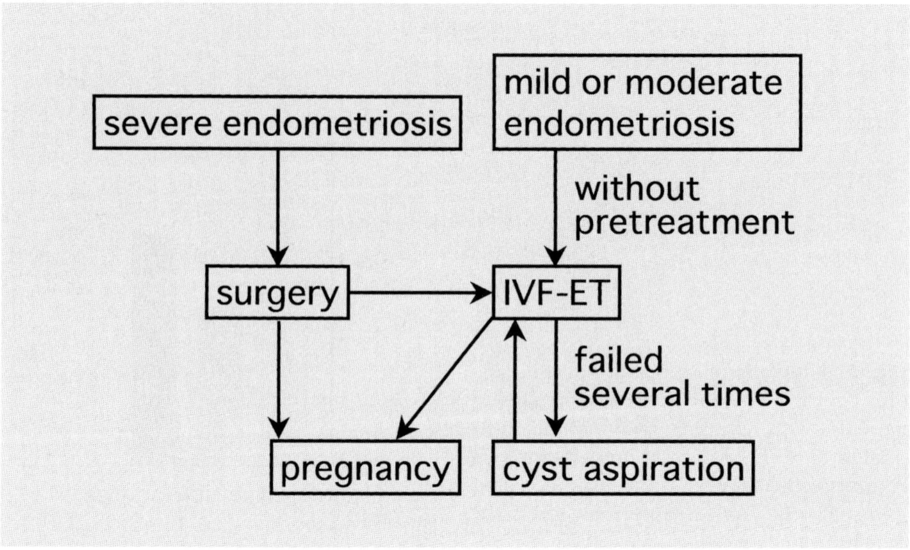

Fig. 3. Treatment of infertile patients with endometriomas.

no extensive resection of ovarian tissues should be performed. For moderate or mild endometriosis cases, ART is indicated without any surgical pretreatments. After several failed IVF-ET attempts, the content of endometrioma will be aspirated before the next IVF procedure.

Acknowledgements

We thank the staff of each participating hospital for performing the ART procedures, and Dr. Junko Goto (Hamamatsu University School of Medicine) and Ms. Hisae Mizuno for preparing the manuscript.

References

1 Japan Society of Obstetrics and Gynecology: Assisted reproductive technology in Japan: 1999 results generated from the Japan Society of Obstetrics and Gynecology for assisted reproductive technology registry (in Japanese). Acta Obstet Gynaecol Japon 2001;53:1462–1493.
2 Burns WN, Schenken RS: Pathophysiology of endometriosis-associated infertility. Clin Obstet Gynecol 1999;42:586–610.
3 Suganuma N, Moriwaki T, Ando T, Narita O, Osawa M, Tanaka T, Saito H, Seki M, Tsutsumi O, Kanzaki H, Hoshiai A, Yamano S, Nagata Y, Matsuura K, Okamura H: Effects of danazol pretreatment for patients with endometriosis on their in vitro fertilization and embryo transfer outcomes; in Minaguchi H, Sugimoto O (eds): Endometriosis Today. Lancs, Parthenon Publishing, 1997, pp 392–397.
4 Pellicer A, Albert C, Garrido N, Navarro J, Remohi J, Simon C: The pathophysiology of endometriosis-associated infertility: follicular environment and embryo quality. J Reprod Fertil 2000;55(suppl):109–119.
5 Nakamura K, Oosawa M, Kondou I, Inagaki S, Shibata H, Narita O, Suganuma N, Tomoda Y: Menotropin stimulation after prolonged gonadotropin releasing hormone agonist pretreatment for in vitro fertilization in patients with endometriosis. J Assist Reprod Genet 1992;9: 113–117.
6 Suganuma N, Asada Y, Yamamoto M, Moriwaki T, Kitagawa T, Tomoda Y, Mishima A, Miyake K: Successful pregnancy after intracytoplasmic injection of a single testicular spermatozoon into a human oocyte: a case report. J Obstet Gynaecol Res 1996;22:111–117.
7 Dlugi AM, Loy RA, Dieterle S, Bayer SR, Seibel MM: The effect of endometriomas on in vitro fertilization outcome. J In Vitro Fert Embryo Transf 1989;6:338–341.
8 Olivennes F, Feldberg D, Liu HC, Cohen J, Moy F, Rosenwaks Z: Endometriosis: A stage-by-stage analysis – The role of in vitro fertilization. Fertil Steril 1995;64:392–398.
9 Yanushpolsky EH, Best CL, Jackson KV, Clarke RL, Barbieri RL, Hornstein MD: Effects of endometriosis on oocyte quality, embryo quality, and pregnancy rates in in vitro fertilization cycles: a prospective case-controlled study. J Assist Reprod Genet 1998;15: 193–197.
10 Isaacs JD Jr, Hines RS, Sopelak VM, Cowan BD: Ovarian endometriomas do not adversely affect pregnancy success following treatment with in vitro fertilization. J Assist Reprod Genet 1997;14:551–553.
11 Dokras A, Olive DL: Endometriosis and assisted reproductive technologies. Clin Obstet Gynecol 1999;42:687–698.
12 Soong YK, Chang FH, Chou HH, Chang MY, Lee CL, Lai YM, Chang SY: Life table analysis of pregnancy rates in women with moderate or severe endometriosis comparing danazol therapy after carbon dioxide laser laparoscopy plus electrocoagulation or laparotomy plus electrocoagulation versus danazol therapy only. J Am Assoc Gynecol Laparosc 1997;4:225–230.
13 Adamson GD, Pasta DJ: Surgical treatment of endometriosis-associated infertility: meta-analysis compared with survival analysis. Am J Obstet Gynecol 1994;171:1488–1504.
14 Pagidas K, Falcone T, Hemmings R, Miron P: Comparison of reoperation for moderate (stage III) and severe (stage IV) endometriosis-related infertility with in vitro fertilization-embryo transfer. Fertil Steril 1996;65:791–795.

Post-Presentation Discussion

Professor Hoshiai: Thank you very much, Dr. Suganuma, for this very nice presentation. The paper is now open for discussion.

Dr. Kubota: Dr. Suganuma, you compared pretreatment by surgery and cyst aspiration with no treatment and IVF-ET. How about medical pretreatment, for example, danazol or GnRH agonist? Do you have any data on that?

Dr. Suganuma: Today I did not present such data because the numbers are somewhat limited. It is very hard to divide such cases involving long-term danazol, or maybe long-term GnRH agonist, or even short-term treatment. As presented here, no-treatment cases indicated a complete lack of treatment, usually directly to IVF-ET. In other cases, for example, surgery cases, we usually administer GnRH agonist treatment. Long-term treatment is performed until the IVF is started. During this period, GnRH agonist or some other medication is usually given to such patients.

Dr. Kubota: How about the results of an ultralong protocol using GnRH agonist over the course of two or three months compared to other protocols?

Dr. Suganuma: In the present study, I do not have any data on this difference. However, previously I reported that an ultralong protocol for patients with endometriosis is more effective before IVF-ET. I think it may be effective in suppressing the endometriosis. However, in this study, I have no data on that.

Dr. Osuga: The effect of endometrioma treatment on follicular growth or oocyte quality differs depending on whether the endometrioma is on the same side or on the opposite side. When the endometrioma is on the same side, follicular growth and oocyte quality are affected by some anatomical factor, such as blood supply, whereas contralateral ovaries are affected by some indirect factor, such as via cytokines. Did you analyze the effect of surgery or aspiration based on such data?

Dr. Suganuma: There are many reports of substances affecting oocyte quality or embryo quality, and some substances produced from the endometriotic cells, such as cytokines, may also affect oocyte quality. As you know, some surgical treatments to reduce the endometrioma mass have a positive effect on oocyte quality. However, in this study, some good results were observed, as when patients with endometrioma went directly to IVF-ET. Endometriosis is very difficult to detect before laparoscopy, and can only be found by ultrasonic imaging. When I find such endometrioma, I would like to determine the best treatment approach. One negative factor in such cases is that in addition to the endometrioma, there is also often some peritoneal endometriosis in endometriotic lesions. However, when I do IVF, the oocyte is retrieved from the body, fertilized and returned to the uterus, and with this procedure, we can achieve a good pregnancy rate. Some substances present in the pelvic cavity, which have a negative effect on the pregnancy rate, are avoided by removing the oocyte from the body. So if you have the plan to do IVF-ET as a treatment of infertility, I think there is no need for such a hard treatment for the patient.

Dr. Osuga: So, in your data, both bilateral and unilateral endometrioma are included. If you separate the data based on unilateral endometrioma and bilateral endometrioma, are there any differences in the pregnancy rate?

Dr. Suganuma: Our data includes 36 cases treated by surgery and 21 of those cases were by laparoscopic treatment. I cannot give any details regarding the comparison of bilateral and unilateral cases.

Professor Donnez: I have some comments, some of which have already been raised by previous discussants. In the group of no treatment, a literature search reveals that 30% of the patients have only a luteal cyst, and no endometrioma. In the absence of biopsy and laparoscopy, the no-treatment group is not a pure group. We have no proof that it is endometriosis.

Dr. Suganuma: Every case in the no-treatment group was endometrioma. I confirmed the presence of endometriotic cells from the ovary when I did IVF-ET. I aspirated the content of the cyst and confirmed this with the histological analysis.

Professor Donnez: Which type of analysis? Cytology? Do you observe endometrial cells or just chocolate fluid?

Dr. Suganuma: I receive a report from the histological pathologist, which states that endometrial cells are present. Whenever I find, for example, some clear fluid, those cases are excluded.

Professor Donnez: Chocolate fluid does not necessarily mean endometrioma. In some cases, it is a luteal cyst. My next comment is that I disagree with your second conclusion. You state that in the group of patients with no treatment, the quality of the oocyte was very good. I don't think that we can say that from your study. On the contrary, if I were writing the article, I would say that the quality of oocytes is significantly lower in that group, because although the mean number of oocytes was 8 in that group, there was a significant difference in the fertilization rate. The fertilization rate is lower in the group of patients without any therapy, which suggests, as I believe you noted, a possible toxic effect from the endometrioma. It is not true that the quality of the oocyte is the same. The biologist has observed a lot of mature, metaphase II oocytes, but there is a significant difference going from 8 oocytes to 5 embryos, and this suggests a toxic effect.

Dr. Suganuma: As you say there may be some toxic effect from the endometriotic cell in endometrioma. However, I have only presented here an analysis of the metaphase II oocyte rate. We defined metaphase II as a mature oocyte. We cannot make any more detailed comments on the quality of the oocyte. As I showed in my presentation, the fertilization rate is also not so good, compared to the cyst-aspirated group. Some toxic effect may have occurred in the no-treatment group. The thing that I would like to suggest is that if we have some cases without any treatment in which IVF failed, we can do the cyst aspiration after that, and maybe there will be a good effect that will improve the quality of the oocyte.

Professor Donnez: In Europe, there has been a consensus on ovarian endometrioma that the first line of therapy for endometrioma must be surgical removal, even if IVF has been proposed. The three reasons for this are the risk of increasing the size of the endometrioma by several attempts of IVF, the risk or rupture of the ovarian endometrioma due to the quick increase, which we have also observed recently, and finally, the high rate of pregnancy, over 50%, which can be achieved after simply removing the endometrioma. Thus, the consensus has been that in cases of ovarian endometrioma, the first line of therapy is surgery. If after one year the patient is not pregnant, and as I mentioned before, about 50% of the patients will not get pregnant, then there is a 50% progression to IVF, where after 2 or 3 attempts, you can also probably expect a 50–60% rate of pregnancy. This means that the total number of women with endometrioma who will achieve a pregnancy in cases of ovarian endometrioma is nearly 80%. Thus, I don't think it is wise to propose going immediately to IVF. I am a little bit concerned about such an approach in cases of ovarian endometrioma, given that you can do the surgery easily by laparoscopy.

Dr. Suganuma: I think that it depends on the size of the endometrioma or the patient's symptoms. In Japan, there may indeed be some big hospitals that can do laparoscopy very easily, but certainly clinics are not set up to do laparoscopy.

Professor Donnez: I see a lot of young gynecologists at this conference and there is an obvious interest in endometriosis. I am sure that the average surgeon's skill in laparoscopy will develop in Japan, as well as in Belgium and elsewhere in Europe. Laparoscopy is a new tool that we will have to try and develop.

Dr. Suganuma: I agree with you. However, we have some private clinics in Japan that do IVF mainly. For example, one big private clinic does 6,000 IVF cycles per year, and such clinics are not equipped to do laparoscopy. I think it has to be a collaboration between clinics and hospitals.

Professor Donnez: In Europe, we have observed a significant decrease in the number of people asking for IVF. I am sure that you will observe a similar decrease very soon in Japan. People are asking more and more to come back and to try and get pregnant by sexual intercourse, even if they have to go through surgery. That's a balance, a pendulum.

Session 4
Review

Gynecologic and Obstetric Investigation

Gynecol Obstet Invest 2002;54(suppl 1):43–51
DOI: 10.1159/000066294

Diagnosis and Imaging of Adenomyotic Disease of the Retroperitoneal Space

Jean Squifflet[a] Chantal Feger[b] Jacques Donnez[a]

Departments of [a]Gynecology and [b]Radiology, Université Catholique de Louvain, Brussels, Belgium

Key Words
Adenomyotic · Retroperitoneal space · MRI · Transrectal ultrasonography

Abstract
This manuscript discusses the diagnosis and imaging of adenomyotic disease of the retroperitoneal space, a pathology that we have defined as retroperitoneal adenomyotic disease (RAD). By prospective analysis, comparing barium enema, magnetic resonance imaging (MRI) and transrectal ultrasonography, we distinguished three types of retroperitoneal adenomyotic lesions. The most frequently encountered types were posterior vaginal fornix lesions, followed by hourglass-shaped or diabolo-like lesions, and then by rectovaginal septum lesions. This anatomical classification based on clinical examination and imaging will allow us in the future to define the most appropriate treatment for each entity.

Introduction

The concept of retroperitoneal adenomyotic disease (RAD) was born in 1998, and first published in 2001 by Donnez and his team [1]. We suggested that the retroperitoneal space be considered as the origin of adenomyotic disease, and banished the concept of deep-infiltrating endometriosis. Our hypothesis is that these lesions result from metaplasia of Müllerian rests. Smooth muscle proliferation of fibrosis, which is consistently observed, is responsible for the nodular aspect of these lesions located in the rectovaginal septum, or behind the cervix. These lesions are retroperitoneal and may extend laterally or to the anterior rectal wall, provoking perivisceritis. This perivisceritis phenomenon, visible at radiography, is not a rectal endometriotic lesion or invasion of the rectal wall by the endometriotic process, as has been suggested by many investigators. In our opinion, it is only the consequence of serosal retraction caused by the inflammatory process or fibrosis of the anterior wall of the rectum due to an adenomyotic lesion.

How Can It Be Diagnosed?

The first step in the diagnosis of this pathology is a clinical examination; a very thorough medical history has to be obtained, the principal features of this pathology being pelvic pain and infertility. Unfortunately, most women with adenomyotic lesions suffer for a long time. Adenomyotic nodules of the rectovaginal septum could involve the uterosacral ligaments, posterior vaginal wall, posterior fornix, and sometimes extension to the anterior rectal wall or the distal part of the ureter [2].

In cases of severe lesions, the pouch of Douglas could be completely or partially obliterated. Symptoms in this case are generally pelvic pain, deep dyspareunia, depending on the position adopted during sexual intercourse, and

KARGER
Fax + 41 61 306 12 34
E-Mail karger@karger.ch
www.karger.com

0378–7346/02/0545–0043$18.50/0

Accessible online at:
www.karger.com/goi

Jacques Donnez, MD, PhD
Department of Gynecology, Catholic University of Louvain
Cliniques Universitaires St-Luc, Avenue Hippocrate 10
B–1200 Brussels (Belgium)
Tel. +32 2 764 9502, Fax +32 2 764 9507, E-Mail donnez@gyne.ucl.ac.be

Table 1. Additional examinations in 35 women with retroperitoneal adenomyotic disease

	Rectovaginal septum (n = 5)	Posterior vaginal fornix (n = 21)	'Hourglass'-shaped (n = 9)
Positive bowel barium enema	1/5	10/21	8/9
Transrectal ultrasonography	5/5	21/21	7/9[a]
MRI	3/5[b]	21/21	9/9

[a] Transrectal ultrasonography found adenomyotic lesions in the remaining two patients, but did not conclusively establish a typical hourglass-shaped lesion.
[b] MRI did not reveal any adenomyotic lesions in the two remaining cases. On clinical examination, these lesions were found to be <2 cm in size.

dyschezia. At least 50% of patients have a past history of one episode of pelvic surgery without the correct diagnosis.

A clinical examination with the help of a speculum is carried out to locate bluish lesions behind the cervix. The fingers constitute one of the most important diagnostic tools, allowing bi-manual vaginal examination with careful examination of the posterior part of the cervix and posterior wall of the vagina. The size of the lesions must be evaluated, as well as their location (medial or lateral to the uterosacral ligament) because lateral localization of the pathology could indicate possible extension to the ureter. The aim of additional procedures is to confirm the diagnosis of adenomyotic nodules and other entities, e.g. endometriotic cysts, adenomyotic lesions of the uterus or adenomyotic lesions of the bladder. Laparoscopic exploration could sometimes underestimate the presence and extension of the adenomyotic nodule if the correct diagnosis is not made before. Preoperative imaging is therefore needed to establish the correct diagnosis and extension of the adenomyotic nodule into the rectovaginal space.

In this manuscript, we review a prospective series of 35 women with retroperitoneal adenomyotic disease in order to evaluate prospectively additional examinations: barium enema, transrectal echography, and magnetic resonance imaging (MRI).

Bowel Barium Enema

A double contrast bowel barium enema in a profile view of the rectosigmoid junction may be able to detect a mass effect or perivisceritis of the anterior wall of the rectum in cases of adenomyotic lesions. Very careful examination of this profile view in good conditions was able to detect a mass effect in 54% of cases (table 1). A decrease in inflation of the rectal ampulla is the first indirect sign of adenomyotic lesions (fig. 1a). In cases involving more extensive lesions, an irregular aspect of the anterior wall could reflect perivisceritis extended to the anterior wall (fig. 1b). Contrast barium enema may also identify upper bowel lesions as true endometriotic lesions of the sigmoid wall, which are not considered as adenomyotic lesions and require different treatment.

Transrectal Ultrasonography

Different types of transducers can be used. Fedele et al. [3] used an ultrasound scanner with a biplane two-dimensional axial and sagittal convex 6.5-MHz probe. The advantage of this rigid probe is very good visualization of the uterosacral ligaments and small adenomyotic lesions; the disadvantage is that the probe is rigid and cannot explore the upper part of the sigmoid (no higher than the rectosigmoid junction).

Roscau et al. [4] used rectal endoscopic ultrasonography with 7.5-MHz and 12.5-MHz probes, allowing circumferential imaging of the rectum and surrounding areas. These probes permit a complete circumferential analysis of the adjacent border of the rectal wall, as in the case of malignant lesions of the rectum, to establish the depth of infiltration of the rectal muscularis proprius. Unfortunately, their sensitivity appears to be lower for smaller adenomyotic lesions without any involvement of the bowel wall, like uterosacral lesions. The flexible nature of the echo-endoscope allows the transducer to be positioned in the distal sigmoid, and therefore it can diagnose true upper endometriotic lesions of the sigmoid.

In our department, transrectal ultrasonography was performed using a Corevision Pro (Toshiba®, Japan, Endocavitary Transducer PVL-715RT, linear and convex transducer head) ultrasound scanner with a biplane two-dimensional longitudinal axial and sagittal circumferential 7-MHz probe. A water-filled balloon was placed over

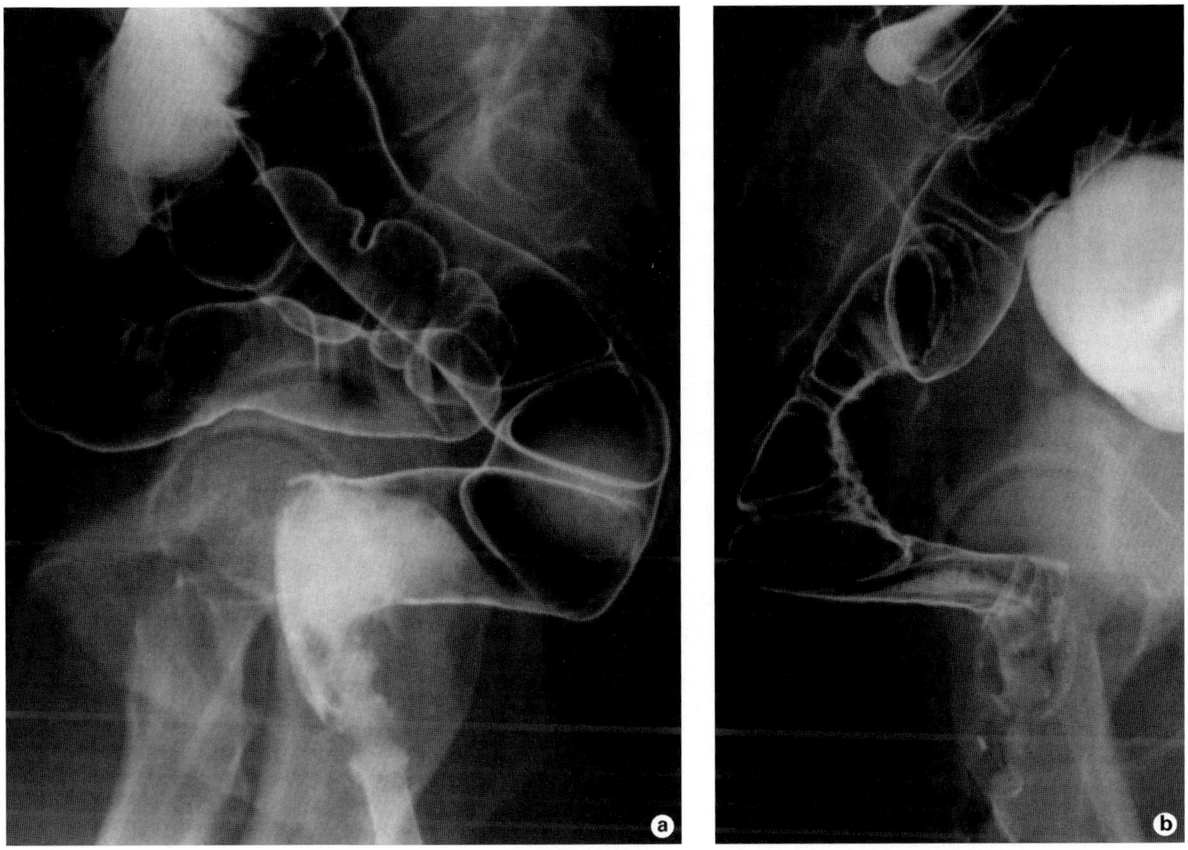

Fig. 1. Bowel barium enema: profile view of the rectum in double contrast; (**a**) normal anterior wall; (**b**) large perivisceritis along the anterior rectal wall.

the tip of the probe to obtain contrast to evaluate the infiltration of the rectal wall. The transducer was inserted into the rectum and advanced until the midline image of the cervix was visualized, using the longitudinal view. The vagina, uterine cervix, parametrium, uterosacral ligaments and rectal wall were evaluated by moving the transducer along its longitudinal axis and rotating it. In the sagittal view, the ultrasonographer could delimit and measure the lesions. In the circumferential view, lateral extension of the lesions to the uterosacral ligaments could easily be determined (fig. 2a).

Typical adenomyotic lesions look like pure hypoechogenic cystic lesions surrounded by irregular, less hypoechogenic structures; these well-circumscribed small focal lesions correspond to dilatation of the endometriotic glands surrounded by smooth muscle hyperplasia. In some cases, these lesions produce a mass effect. All these retroperitoneal lesions were found to be located either attached to the cervix, in the rectovaginal septum or extending to the anterior wall of the rectum (fig. 2b).

Visualization of the integrity of the rectovaginal septum as a linear hyperechogenic structure could exclude infiltration of the rectal wall. When a continuum was observed as a hypoechogenic structure between the rectal muscularis proprius and the adenomyotic nodule, extension of the lesion to the anterior wall was diagnosed (fig. 3).

In cases of lateral extension and to evaluate the possibility of true ureteral lesions, Doppler ultrasound of the bladder was performed to prove normal bilateral ureteral flow.

When the Douglas area was observed to contain liquid, or bowel contractions and movement were noted in this area, it was considered as an indirect sign of the absence of adhesions. However, if no liquid or motion were observed, obliteration of the Douglas pouch could be suspected. Endometriotic cysts in the ovaries could easily be seen, especially when there were kissing ovaries or if the patient was a virgin.

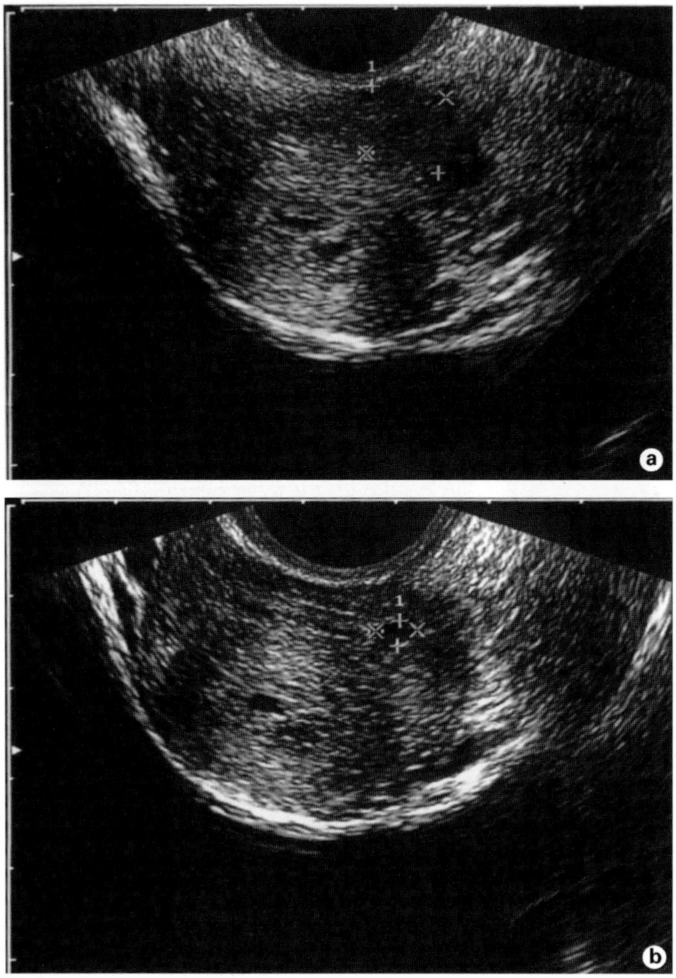

Fig. 2. (**a**) Transrectal ultrasonography of a uterosacral adenomyotic lesion; (**b**) hypoechogenic well-circumscribed lesions.

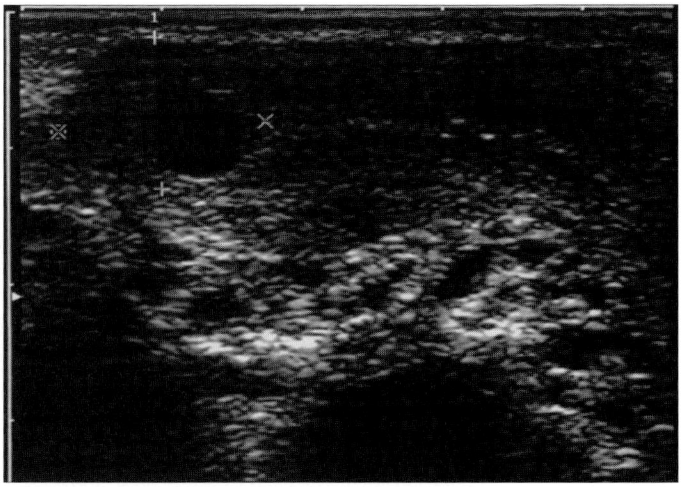

Fig. 3. Ultrasonography: sagittal view; the linear probe is along the top.

A transrectal ultrasonography could also detect adenomyotic nodules of the bladder, situated medially just above the bladder trigone.

Magnetic Resonance Imaging (fig. 4a–d)

MRI can diagnose endometriotic lesions as hypointense areas surrounding hyperintense spots in the myometrium in T2-weighted spin echo images and some hyperintense spots after intravenous injection of gadolinium agent in T1-weighted spin echo images. In addition, bladder and rectovaginal adenomyosis may be detected by MRI [5]. Retroperitoneal lesions are characterized on MRI by small hyperintense signals, surrounded by hypointense areas in axial and sagittal T2-weighted fast spin echo images. Axial T1-weighted spin echo images, from the symphysis to the aortic bifurcation, were also obtained. Contrast enhanced T1- and T2-weighted fat-suppressed spin echo images after intravenous injection of gadolinium agent were realized in the same axis to complete the diagnosis of adenomyotic nodules and determine the presence of other endometriotic lesions in the pelvis.

Retroperitoneal adenomyotic lesions are better visualized in T2-weighted images in a sagittal view, just on the posterior face of the posterior lips of the cervix, in front of the attachment of the vagina to the cervix. All section views perpendicular to the uterine axis are able to demonstrate lateral extension of the lesions to the uterosacral ligaments, as in a neoplastic lesion of the cervix. The extension of the lesions can be towards the uterosacral ligaments, which can cause attraction and substenosis of the ureter due to smooth muscle hyperplasia and the presence of endometriotic glands. This can lead to ureteral stenosis and pyelic dilatation or ureteronephrosis. MRI can also diagnose bladder adenomyotic nodules, and we have demonstrated that bladder endometriosis is also considered to be a retroperitoneal disease [6].

In cases of rectovaginal adenomyotic nodules developing laterally and/or exceeding 3 cm in size, each patient should systematically undergo preoperative intravenous pyelography (IVP). IVP is abnormal in more than 10% of these cases, and can detect small abnormalities of the ureter like medialization, substenosis, lack of distension after decompression, and may suggest the beginning of compression of the ureter by lateral extension of the nodule [2].

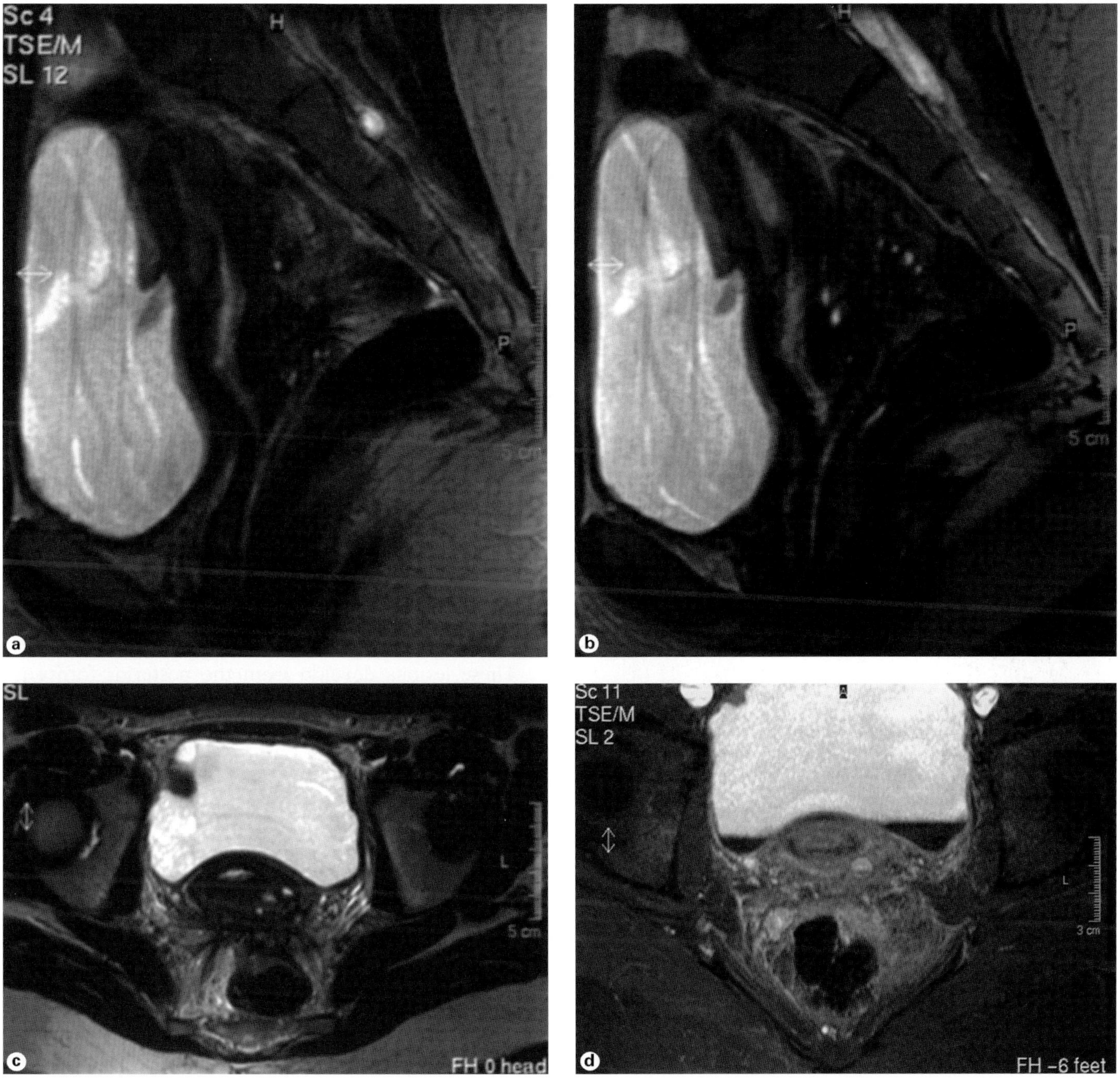

Fig. 4. MRI: (**a**) sagittal view in T2-weighted spin echo images, (**b**) idem, (**c**) axial view in T2, and (**d**) axial view in T1-weighted fat sat and gadolinium.

Discussion

Koninckx and Martin [7] proposed a classification based on three types: type 1, type 2, and type 3. Type 3 was suggested to be adenomyosis. Adamyan's classification attempted to describe the lesions anatomically [8]. More recently, Vercellini et al. [9] proposed that intraperitoneal endometriosis could explain the obliteration of the rectovaginal pouch and the subsequent infiltration of the rectovaginal septum by the lesions. That is why the term 'deep-infiltrating disease' is sometimes used to describe these lesions. This latter hypothesis, however, has neither anatomical nor histopathological support.

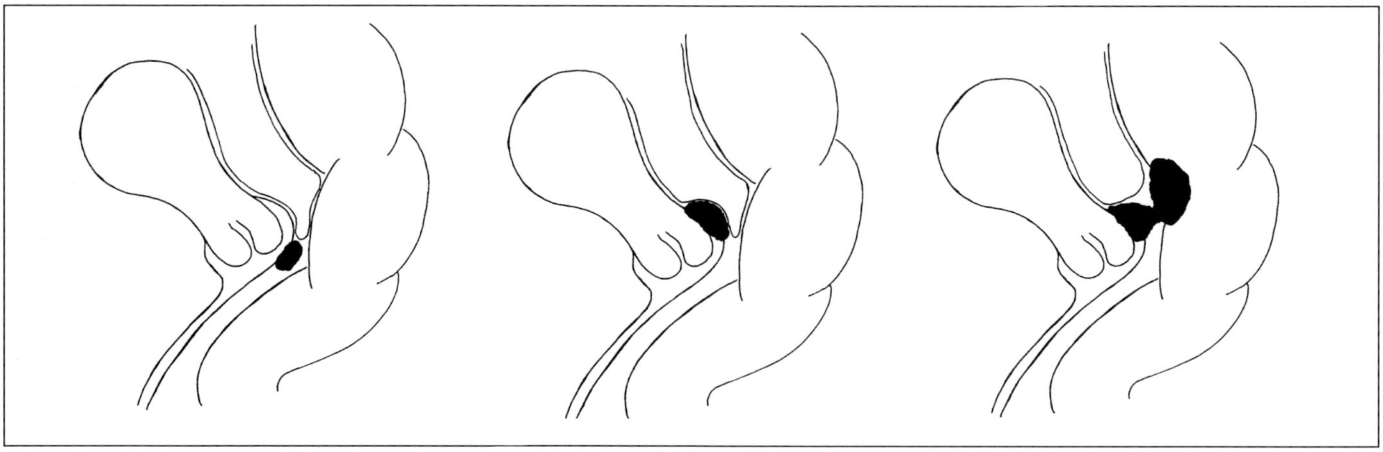

Fig. 5. Classification (from left to right): (1) rectovaginal septum lesion (type I); (2) posterior vaginal fornix lesion (type II); (3) hourglass-shaped lesion (type III).

In our theory, adenomyosis originates in the retrocervical area and involves the retroperitoneal space. That is why we defend this concept. We have proposed a classification that takes into account the location of the retroperitoneal lesion, as precisely defined by transrectal ultrasonography and MRI (fig. 5).

Rectovaginal Septum Lesions

These lesions are situated within the rectovaginal septum between the posterior wall of the vaginal mucosa and the anterior wall of the rectal muscularis (fig. 6). Cranially, the rectovaginal septum is limited by the joining of the two uterosacral ligaments behind the cervix. According to our definition, the lesion is not linked or attached to the cervix. It is situated under the peritoneal fold of the cul-de-sac of Douglas. The caudal portion of the septum is the perineal body. Most cases are located in the cranial part of the septum. This type is due to metaplasia of Müllerian remnants present in the rectovaginal septum. Rectovaginal septum lesions are usually found to be smaller in size. They are distant from the cervix, and their average size estimated by clinical examination is ≤2 cm.

In almost all cases, the barium enema was found to be normal, and all these cases were diagnosed by transrectal ultrasonography. In one case with a positive bowel barium enema, only slight signs of a mass effect were detected. On MRI, these lesions appeared small and difficult to isolate because of a lack of contrast in the rectovaginal septum, and a lack of non-specific hyperintense spots in this area without any surrounding hypointense areas.

Ultrasonography was able to detect all these lesions, even small ones. Even when the rectovaginal septum is thin, the extremely well defined layers (rectal mucosa, rectal muscularis, septum, posterior vaginal mucosa, and the vaginal line of reflection, observed at echography) allow detection of small adenomyotic lesions.

Posterior Vaginal Fornix Lesions

These lesions develop from the posterior fornix towards the rectovaginal septum (fig. 7a). The posterior fornix is retrocervical and corresponds, in the attachment of the vaginal mucosa, to the posterior face of the posterior lip of the cervix. It is limited by the joining of the two uterosacral ligaments behind the cervix; cranially, it is limited by the peritoneal Douglas pouch; posteriorly, it is limited by the anterior wall of the lower third of the rectum. The crossing of the ureter and the uterine artery occurs 10–15 mm from the lateral vaginal fornix. Large posterior fornix lesions can be associated with an extension of the rectovaginal septum. Posterior vaginal fornix lesions were also found to be small, their average size being assessed by clinical examination. When the lesion is less than 2 cm in size, clinically it is usually fixed to the posterior part of the cervix, and there is no extension to the rectovaginal septum or the rectal wall. The barium enema is then normal.

If the clinical evaluation reveals a larger lesion, more than 3 cm in size, there is a greater risk of extension to the rectal wall (barium enema showed perivisceritis in all cases). This continuum between the rectal muscularis and the cervix was found to obliterate the rectovaginal septum cranially.

All these pathologies were correctly diagnosed by transvaginal ultrasonography or MRI (fig. 7b, c).

a b

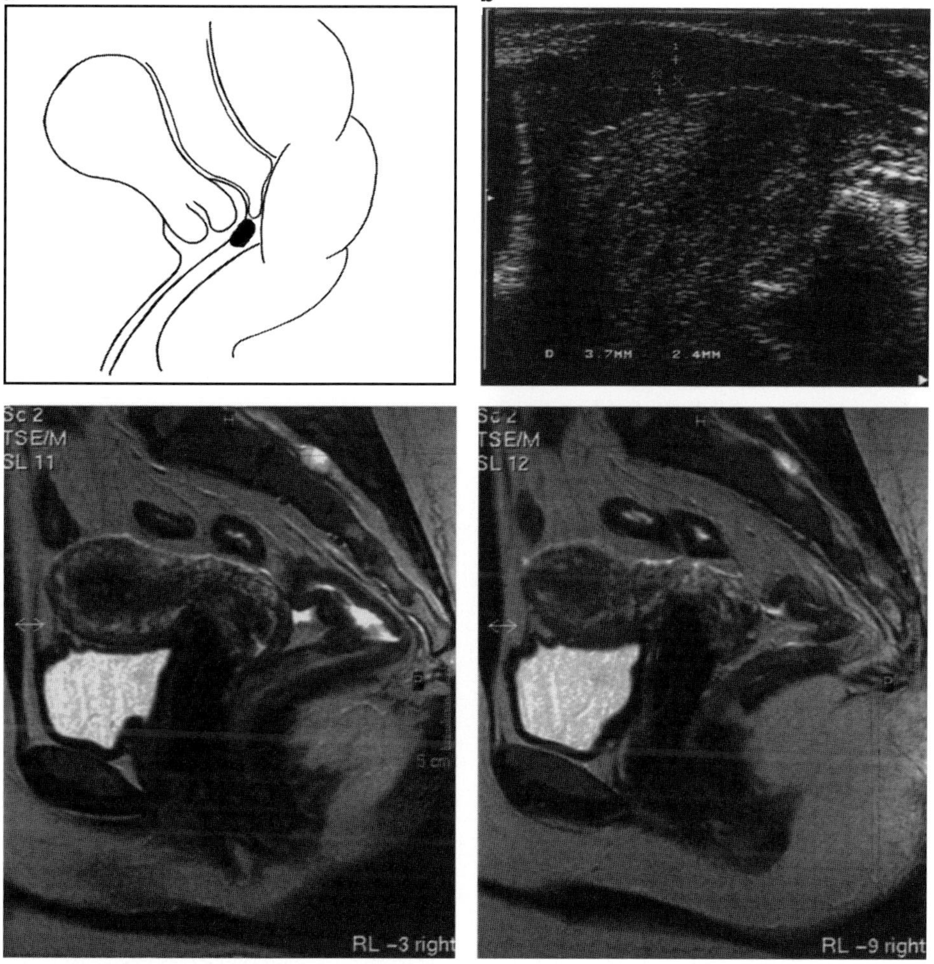

c

Fig. 6. Rectovaginal septum lesion (type I): (**a**) diagram, (**b**) ultrasonography, and (**c**) MRI.

Hourglass-Shaped or Diabolo-Like Lesions

These lesions occur when posterior fornix lesions extend cranially to the anterior rectal wall (fig. 8a). The part of the adenomyotic lesion situated in the anterior rectal wall is the same size as the part of the lesion situated near the posterior fornix. A small but well observed continuum exists between these two parts of the lesion. That is why we have termed these lesions diabolo-like or hourglass-shaped. As noted previously, these lesions always occur under the peritoneal fold of the recto-uterine pouch of Douglas. Hourglass-type lesions were also found to be large, their average size estimated by clinical examination to be 3 cm. Barium enema showed signs of perivisceritis in nearly all cases.

It must be noted that the clinical size of these nodules was similar to that estimated by MRI (fig. 8b), although transrectal ultrasonography underestimated the size of the lesions. Ultrasonography could detect and analyze the infiltration of the rectal muscularis very well in all these cases (fig. 8c). However, due to the greater mass effect and loss of echoes, it was difficult to evaluate the correct size and anatomic description of the adenomyotic lesions, as distinguishing hourglass-shaped and large posterior fornix lesions by echography is not straightforward. In all 9 cases of the hourglass-shaped group, we were able to diagnose adenomyosis and infiltration of the rectal muscularis by echography; however, in 2 cases, we were not able to conclusively establish whether the lesions were indeed hourglass-shaped.

Perivisceritis occurs in all diabolo-like and large posterior vaginal fornix lesions. This process seems to be secondary to the development and growth of the lesion.

The most frequent type, in our experience, is the posterior vaginal fornix lesion in 60% of cases (extension to the rectovaginal septum due to the size in 20% of all cases). Next, come hourglass-shaped or diabolo-like le-

a
b
c

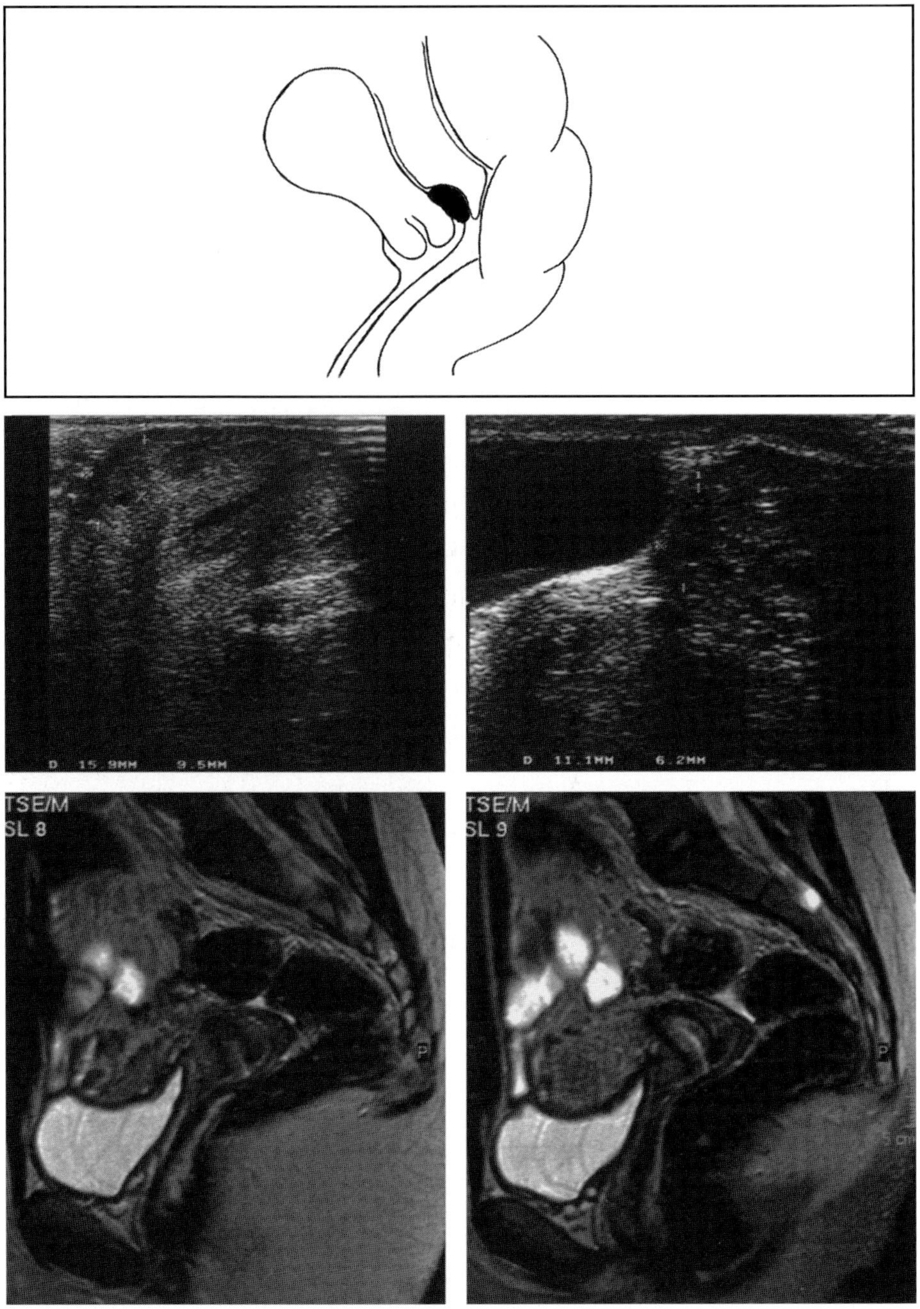

Fig. 7. Posterior vaginal fornix lesion (type II): (**a**) diagram, (**b**) ultrasonography, and (**c**) MRI.

sions in 25% of cases. The most infrequent type of lesion is the rectovaginal septum type in 15% of cases. It is thus inappropriate to systematically call all retroperitoneal lesions 'rectovaginal septum adenomyosis'. Only 15% of them are located in the rectovaginal septum. We therefore suggest classifying the lesions into three types according to their location, clearly defined by clinical examination, transrectal echography and MRI: (1) rectovaginal septum lesions; (2) posterior vaginal fornix lesions; (3) hourglass-shaped or diabolo-like lesions.

This prospective classification demonstrates that even in case of small lesions, the localization of the adenomyotic lesion is either the posterior fornix or the rectovaginal septum. This confirms the need to remove part of the vaginal mucosa to correctly treat the lesion.

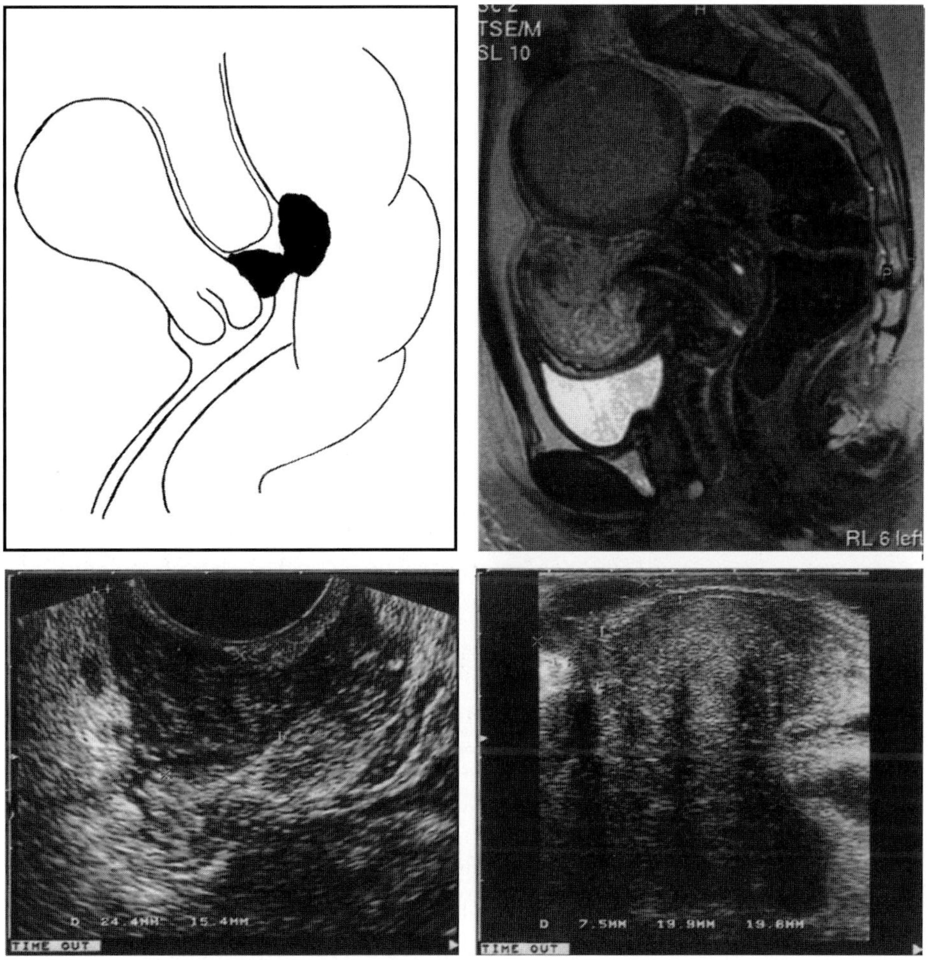

Fig. 8. Hourglass-shaped lesion (type III): (**a**) diagram, (**b**) MRI, (**c**) ultrasonography.

References

1 Donnez J, Donnez O, Squifflet J, Nisolle M: The concept of 'adenomyotic disease of the retroperitoneal space' is born. Gynaecol Endosc 2001;10:91–94.

2 Donnez J, Nisolle M, Squifflet J: Ureteral endometriosis: a complication of rectovaginal endometriotic (adenomyotic) nodules. Fertil Steril 2002;77:32–37.

3 Fedele L, Bianchi S, Portuese A, Borruto F, Dorta M: Transrectal ultrasonography in the assessment of rectovaginal endometriosis. Obstet Gynecol 1998;91:444–448.

4 Roseau G, Dumontier I, Palazzo L, Chapron C, Dousset B, Chaussade S, Dubuisson JB, Couturier D: Rectosigmoid endometriosis: endoscopic ultrasound features and clinical implications. Endoscopy 2000;32:525–530.

5 Balleyguier C, Chapron C, Dubuisson JB, Kinkel K, Fauconnier A, Vieira M, Hélénon O, Menu Y: Comparison of magnetic resonance imaging and transvaginal ultrasonography in diagnosing bladder endometriosis. J Am Assoc Gynecol Laparosc 2002;9:15–23.

6 Donnez J, Spada F, Squifflet J, Nisolle M: Bladder endometriosis must be considered as bladder adenomyosis. Fertil Steril 2000;74:1175–1181.

7 Koninckx PR, Martin D: Deep endometriosis: A consequence of infiltration or retraction or possible adenomyosis externa? Fertil Steril 1992;58:924–928.

8 Adamyan L: Additional international perspectives; in Nichols DH (ed): Gynecologic and Obstetric Surgery. St. Louis, Mosby-Year Book, 1993, pp 1167–1182.

9 Vercellini P, Aimi G, Panazza S, Vicentini S, Pisacreta A, Crosignani PG: Deep endometriosis conundrum: Evidence in favor of a peritoneal origin. Fertil Steril 2000;73:1043–1046.

Special Lecture

Gynecologic and Obstetric Investigation

Gynecol Obstet Invest 2002;54(suppl 1):52–62
DOI: 10.1159/000066295

Current Thinking on the Pathogenesis of Endometriosis

Jacques Donnez Anne Van Langendonckt Françoise Casanas-Roux Jean-Paul Van Gossum Céline Pirard Pascale Jadoul Jean Squifflet Mireille Smets

Department of Gynecology, Catholic University of Louvain, Cliniques Universitaires St-Luc, Brussels, Belgium

Key Words
Endometriosis · Peritoneal · Ovarian · Rectovaginal nodule · Adenomyosis

Abstract
This manuscript is a review of new ideas regarding the pathogenesis of peritoneal endometriosis, ovarian endometriosis, and retroperitoneal adenomyosis. Peritoneal endometriosis, the different aspects of which (black, red and white) represent distinctive steps in the evolutionary process, can be explained by the transplantation theory. Red lesions are the most active and most highly vascularized lesions and are considered to be the first stage of peritoneal endometriosis. The retroperitoneal nodule is an adenomyotic nodule whose histopathogenesis is not related to the implantation of regurgitated endometrial cells but to metaplasia of Müllerian remnants located in the rectovaginal septum. Metaplastic changes of Müllerian rests into adenomyotic glands involving the rectovaginal septum and the retroperitoneal space are responsible for the striking proliferation of the smooth muscle, creating an adenomyomatous appearance similar to that of adenomyosis in the endometrium.

Introduction

In the pelvis, three different forms of endometriosis must be considered: (1) peritoneal endometriosis, (2) ovarian endometriosis, and (3) endometriosis of the rectovaginal septum [1].

Peritoneal Endometriosis

Three essential conditions must be met to consider retrograde menstruation as the explanation for the pathogenesis of pelvic endometriosis [2]. First, endometrial cells must enter the peritoneal cavity through the fallopian tubes. Second, cells within the menstrual debris must be viable and capable of being transplanted into pelvic structures. Third, the anatomic distribution of endometriosis in the pelvic cavity must correlate with the principles of transplantation for exfoliated cells.

Presence, Attachment, Invasion

Numerous studies have demonstrated that reflux of endometrial cells into the peritoneal cavity during menstruation is a common physiologic condition in women

KARGER
Fax + 41 61 306 12 34
E-Mail karger@karger.ch
www.karger.com

0378–7346/02/0545–0052$18.50/0

Accessible online at:
www.karger.com/goi

Jacques Donnez, MD, PhD
Department of Gynaecology, Cliniques Universitaires St-Luc
Avenue Hippocrate 10
B–1200 Brussels (Belgium)
Tel. +32 2 764 9501, Fax +32 2 764 9507, E-Mail donnez@gyne.ucl.ac.be

with patent tubes [3, 4]. The viability of endometrial cells was demonstrated by culture of the menstrual effluent or peritoneal fluid [5, 6]. Experimental studies also proved that endometriosis could be induced by exposure of the pelvis to increased amounts of menstrual discharge [7, 8]. Implantation of endometrial tissue also experimentally induced endometriosis in rabbits [9, 10].

Integrins are cell-surface glycoproteins that act as receptors for extracellular matrix (ECM) proteins. The expression of some integrins has been described in normal endometrium, where they are important in the interactions between glandular and stromal elements [11–13]. The first description of these glycoproteins in endometriotic tissue was given by Foidart et al. in 1993 [11]. The attachment of endometrial tissue fragments to the peritoneum could be explained by the detection of such cell adhesion molecules.

After the adherence of endometriotic cells to the basement membrane (peritoneum), local degradation of the ECM is required. Recently, Marbaix et al. [14, 15] and Kokorine et al. [16] demonstrated that the marked decline in P concentration at the end of the menstrual cycle would initiate the synthesis and activation of matrix metalloproteinases (MMPs), causing ECM breakdown, tissue collapse and menstruation. Thus, the presence of collagenases was proved during the menstrual period, and their probable presence in the peritoneal fluid, together with regurgitated endometrial cells, could be one of the elements in the local degradation of the peritoneal ECM.

Kokorine et al. [17] detected the presence of MMPs in red peritoneal lesions and ovarian endometriomas independent of the menstrual cycle, suggesting that such lesions could represent shedding independent of the decline in P concentration. This hypothesis was bolstered by the detection of the aminoterminal propeptide of type III procollagen in peritoneal fluid, which is a sign of an increase in the metabolism of the ECM [18].

In vitro studies demonstrated that the invasion index of endometriotic cells was similar to that of bladder metastatic cell lines, suggesting that the invasiveness of endometriotic cells may contribute to the pathogenesis of endometriosis [19].

The anatomic distribution of endometriosis in the pelvic cavity was described by Jenkins et al. [20] and correlated with the principles of transplantation for exfoliated cells. These data suggest that any exposure of the pelvic peritoneum to menstrual reflux would result in an increased risk of endometriosis.

Red, Black and White Lesions

In red flame-like lesions biopsied together with the surrounding normal peritoneum, we observed an extensive vascular network between the stroma recently implanted onto the peritoneal surface and the peritoneal and subperitoneal layers, demonstrating the importance of angiogenesis in the early stages of development after implantation [21, 22]. In our opinion, vascularization of endometriotic implants is probably one of the most important factors of growth and invasion of other tissue by endometrial glands [23, 24].

It seems reasonable to say that angiogenic factors present in the peritoneal fluid of 58% of women with endometriosis facilitate the growth of endometriotic implants. These angiogenic factors could be produced by peritoneal macrophages, retrogradely menstruated endometrial cells, or the ectopic endometriotic lesions themselves [25].

Data from our group [17] revealed the presence of MMPs in the stroma of red lesions throughout the menstrual cycle, although in eutopic endometrium, MMPs are detected only during the marked decline in P. After this partial shedding, the remaining red lesion always regrows constantly until the next shedding, but menstrual shedding finally induces an inflammatory reaction, provoking a scarification process that encloses the implant. The enclosed implant becomes a 'black' lesion because of the presence of intraluminal debris. This scarification process is probably responsible for the reduction in vascularization, as proved by the significant decrease in the relative surface areas of the capillaries and stroma [23].

Oxidative Stress and Peritoneal Endometriosis

Given that retrograde menstruation can be considered a physiologic occurrence in menstruating women with patent tubes [3], how can we explain the fact that not all women are found to have endometriosis at laparoscopy? Endometriosis is a multifactorial disease associated with a general inflammatory response in the peritoneal cavity. Oxidative stress has been proposed as a potential factor involved in the pathophysiology of the disease [26]. Reactive oxygen species have been implicated in the pathogenesis of many human diseases and aging [27, 28].

Reactive oxygen species are intermediaries produced by normal oxygen metabolism. To protect themselves from the deleterious effects of reactive oxygen species, cells have developed a wide range of antioxidant systems to limit production of reactive oxygen species, inactivate them, and repair cell damage. However, oxidative stress may occur when the balance between reactive oxygen species production and antioxidant defense is disrupted. The increasing number of diseases associated with oxidative stress suggests that oxidative balance may be precarious [27].

Origin of Oxidative Stress in the Peritoneal Cavity

Several hypotheses have been proposed to explain why oxidative stress is induced in cases of pelvic endometriosis. Erythrocytes [29], apoptotic endometrial tissue and cell debris [30] transplanted into the peritoneal cavity by menstrual reflux and macrophages [30] have been implicated as potential inducers of oxidative stress. Excessive production of reactive oxygen species may also result from exposure to environmental toxicants and heavy metals, which may disrupt the balance of pro-oxidants and antioxidants. Macrophages, endometriotic lesions, and peritoneal cells of patients with endometriosis show typical features of iron-overloaded tissue; specifically, they are heavily laden with hemosiderin [24, 31, 32]. Several authors have suggested that hemosiderin is formed when abundant ferritin cores come into close contact after partial digestion of their protein coat by lysosomal-siderosome enzymes [33, 34]. In patients with endometriosis, the presence of tissue iron deposits in the peritoneum appears to be related to the presence of endometriotic lesions, since the rate of deposits encountered was higher in peritoneum close to a lesion than in normal-looking peritoneum [35].

Compelling evidence suggests that oxidative stress is increased in women with pelvic endometriosis [26]. Oxidative stress occurs when there is an imbalance between production of reactive oxygen species, which are intermediaries released by normal oxygen metabolism, and antioxidant systems, which are designed to control production of reactive oxygen species, inactivate reactive oxygen species, and repair cell damage. Production of reactive oxygen species appears to be increased in women in whom endometriosis is developing, as indicated by the increased release of reactive oxygen species by macrophages, higher levels of oxidized low-density lipoproteins and their by-products in peritoneal fluid, and overexpression, by endometrial cells, of enzymes that produce reactive oxygen species, such as xanthine oxidase and nitric oxide synthase. Several studies have reported that antioxidant defenses may be altered in endometriosis, as suggested by aberrant expression of endometrial antioxidant enzymes and lower levels of the antioxidant vitamin E in peritoneal fluid. A review of these studies has recently been published in *Fertility and Sterility* [26].

Further studies are warranted to assess the contribution of oxidative stress to the physiopathology of endometriosis. It would be particularly valuable to determine whether antioxidant treatment of endometriosis is effective. Use of mifepristone to treat endometriosis has had promising results [36]. This agent has been shown to inhibit endometrial cell growth, an effect that appears to be due to its antioxidant properties. Reactive oxygen species have also been increasingly studied as regulators of protein activity and inducers of gene expression [37]. As a potential inducer of NF-κB, which activates genes involved in cell adhesion, secretion of inflammatory cytokines, and recruitment of macrophages, oxidative stress may help to trigger the chain of events that leads to the development of endometriotic lesions. Further studies are needed to examine the potential involvement of oxidative stress in the pathophysiology of endometriosis.

Retrocervical or Rectovaginal Adenomyosis: The Retroperitoneal Form of the Disease

In recent studies, we described the differences observed between peritoneal and nodular lesions and suggested that the nodule is not the consequence of deep-infiltrating endometriosis, but is the same as an adenomyotic nodule, which develops from Müllerian rests by metaplasia [1, 2, 21, 22, 39, 40]. Smooth-muscle proliferation and fibrosis, consistently observed, are responsible for the nodular aspect of endometriosis located in the rectovaginal septum. The clinical diagnosis is made only when smooth-muscle proliferation is sufficient to be felt by vaginal examination.

The endometriotic nodule of the rectovaginal septum was considered by Koninckx and Martin [41] to be the consequence of deep-infiltrating endometriosis, and these investigators described three subtypes of deep endometriosis according to the depth of infiltration. The rectovaginal septum endometriotic nodule was considered to be the deepest form of endometriosis and to result from the natural evolution of peritoneal endometriosis in some women.

For us, the nodule of the rectovaginal septum is a different entity from peritoneal endometriosis, which has another pathogenesis, and we strongly suggest that it cor-

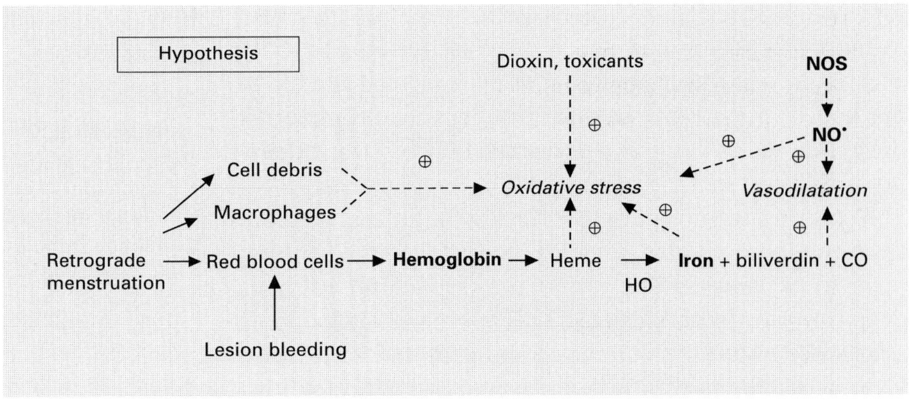

Fig. 1. Hypotheses explaining oxidative stress in the peritoneal cavity of women with endometriosis. Bold type indicates factors that have been studied specifically in relation to pelvic endometriosis. CO = Carbon dioxide; HO = heme oxygenase; NO = nitric oxide; NOS = nitric oxide synthase.

responds to an adenomyotic nodule originating from Müllerian rests by a process of metaplasia [21, 22, 24, 38–40].

Adenomyosis may not respond to physiologic levels of P, and secretory changes are frequently absent or incomplete during the second half of the menstrual cycle. Similar histologic observations can be made at the level of the endometriotic rectovaginal nodule, which is, like an adenomyoma, a circumscribed nodular aggregate of smooth muscle, endometrial glands and, usually endometrial stroma [24, 38, 40]. This lesion originates from the tissue of the retrocervical area or from the rectovaginal septum and consists essentially of smooth muscle with active glandular epithelium and scanty stroma.

Invasion of the smooth muscle by active glandular epithelium without stroma proves that the stroma is not mandatory for invasion and that the nodule is different from peritoneal endometriosis, in which epithelial glands are surrounded systematically by endometrial-type stroma [21, 22]. The similarity of the histologic description to uterine adenomyosis has led us to suggest, like Brosens [42], that the so-called endometriotic nodule of the rectovaginal septum is the same as an adenomyoma or an adenomyotic nodule. Nevertheless, the coexpression of vimentin and cytokeratin indicates a close relationship with its mesodermal Müllerian origin [21, 22, 40].

Smooth Muscle Proliferation

At least three hypotheses could explain this smooth muscle proliferation: (1) endometriotic foci involving smooth muscle are typically associated with striking proliferation of the smooth muscle, creating an adenomyomatous appearance similar to that of adenomyosis in the endometrium [42]; (2) the endometriotic stroma may exhibit smooth muscle metaplasia, as has been demonstrated within the wall of ovarian endometriotic cysts [43]; and (3) it may be due to modified gene expression induced by toxicants.

When endometriotic glands affect the retroperitoneal space, which contains smooth muscle, smooth muscle proliferation can take place and the nodule thus develops. In some cases, retroperitoneal space invasion provokes perivisceritis, which is not a rectal endometriotic lesion or invasion of the rectal wall by the endometriotic process, as has been suggested by many investigators. In our opinion, it is only the consequence of serosal retraction caused by the inflammatory process and fibrosis on the anterior wall of the rectum.

The absence of evolution of the rectal lesion after removal of the nodule supports our hypothesis concerning its retroperitoneal space origin and strongly suggests that it is not necessary to excise the anterior wall of the rectum in such circumstances [38, 39]. However, excision of the nodule and the vaginal mucosa located in front of it is essential because of the presence of endometriotic glands in contact with the vagina.

Surgical Technique

Deep fibrotic nodular adenomyosis involving the cul-de-sac requires excision of the nodular tissue from the posterior vagina, rectum, posterior cervix, and uterosacral ligaments, as described by Reich et al. [44] and Donnez et al. [40, 45–47]. In our series, attention was first directed toward a complete dissection of the anterior rectum throughout its area of involvement until the loose tissue of the rectovaginal space was reached. A sponge on a ring forceps was inserted into the posterior vaginal fornix and a dilator (Hegar 25) was placed in the rectum. In addition, a cannula was inserted into the endometrial cavity to markedly antevert the uterus. The peritoneum covering the cul-de-sac of Douglas was opened between the 'adenomyotic' lesion and the rectum.

We used a technique of first freeing the anterior rectum from the loose areolar tissue of the rectovaginal septum, prior to excising and/or vaporizing visible and palpable deep fibrotic nodular lesions. This approach was possible even when anterior rectal muscle infiltration was present. Careful dissection was then carried out using the aquadissector and the CO_2 laser for sharp dissection, until the rectum was completely freed and identifiable below the lesion.

Excision of the fibrotic tissue on the side of the rectum was attempted only after the rectal dissection was complete. A partial rectal resection was never performed in our series, except in cases of complete rectal or sigmoidal stenosis (table 1). In cases of deep lesions, the vaginal wall was more or less penetrated by the adenomyosis and excision of part of the vagina was essential. Dissection was performed accordingly, not only with the removal of all visible adenomyotic lesions, but also the vaginal mucosa with at least a 0.5 cm disease-free margin (laterally). Lesions extending completely through the vagina were treated with en bloc laparoscopic resection from the cul-de-sac to the posterior vaginal wall; the pneumoperitoneum was maintained and the posterior vaginal wall was closed vaginally.

The anterior rectum can be reperitonealized by plicating ligaments and lateral rectal peritoneum across the midline using 4-0 Polydioxanone Tissucol® or Interceed® [45–48]. Deep rectal muscle defects can be closed with suture. Full-thickness rectal lesion excisions were successfully repaired with suture in the series of Reich et al. [44].

In our series of 1,125 cases, laparoscopic dissection was performed successfully in all cases, even when radiography of the colon showed bowel involvement. Bowel resection is usually unnecessary, except in cases of bowel occlusion and rectal bleeding. In such cases, resection of the rectosigmoid junction must be carried out. In our series of 1,125 cases, laparoscopic rectal perforation occurred in seven cases. All perforations but one were diagnosed at the time of laparoscopy. In three cases, the rectum was repaired by laparotomy and, in the others, by colpotomy or laparoscopy. During the same period, 21 patients who had rectal endometriosis with stenosis and rectal bleeding were operated on by

Table 1. Rectovaginal adenomyosis

	n	%
Laparoscopic adenomyotic nodule excision	1,125	98.2
Laparotomy: nodule excision with bowel (sigmoidal or rectal) resection and anastomosis in case of bowel substenosis and menstrual rectal bleeding	21	1.8

laparotomy. Bowel resection with anastomosis was then carried out.

When a ureter is close to the lesion, its course can be traced starting at the pelvic brim. The peritoneum overlying the ureter can be opened to confirm the ureteral position deep in the pelvis. In cases of nodular lesions >3 cm, an incidence of nearly 10% of ureteral stenosis was recently demonstrated [48].

Long-Term Results

Table 2 shows the number of patients followed up for more than 3 years in our department. We analyzed the long-term (3–10 years) results, after excluding patients who were referred by foreign centers and those followed up in other countries. Recurrence rates of dysmenorrhea, deep dyspareunia, and nodules were noted according to the surgical technique used (3 groups).

The dysmenorrhea recurrence rates were respectively 29, 17 and 26% in the three groups, but if severe dysmenorrhea was chosen as a criterion, the recurrence rate was significantly lower when excision of the nodule was carried out together with resection of the posterior fornix. The same conclusion can be reached if the severe dyspareunia recurrence rate is analyzed. In our opinion, the better results found in group II can be explained by the wide resection of the posterior vaginal fornix, including the resection of sympathetic nerves situated between the cervix and the uterosacral ligaments (torus uterinum). It is very important to note that the recurrence rates of dysmenorrhea, dyspareunia and nodules were lower in group II (excision of nodules + posterior fornix) than in group III (bowel resection, no vaginal resection). This again proves that very aggressive surgery including bowel resection does not prevent recurrence. Large debulking surgery must be considered more appropriate than extensive surgery, such as bowel resection. Vaginal fornix resection

Table 2. Recurrence of dysmenorrhea, deep dyspareunia and nodules according to the surgical technique used

	Group I (n = 150)[1]	Group II (n = 282)[2]	Group III (n = 15)[3]
Recurrence of dysmenorrhea	43 (29%)	46 (17%)	4 (26%)
Severe	21 (14%)	20 (7.5%)	3 (20%)
Mild or moderate	22 (15%)	26 (9.5%)	1 (6%)
Deep dyspareunia	29 (19%)	35 (13%)	4 (26%)
Severe	22 (15%)	20 (7.5%)	3 (20%)
Mild or moderate	7 (4%)	15 (5.5%)	1 (6%)
Severe pelvic pain	24 (16%)	27 (10%)	3 (20%)
Recurrence of nodules	26 (17.3%)	10 (3.7%)*	3 (20%)
Average interval	4.9 years (3–10 years)	3.8 years (3–6 years)	4.1 years (3–10 years)

1 Excision of the nodule without resection of the vaginal mucosa (laparoscopy).
2 Excision of the nodule with resection of the posterior vaginal fornix (laparoscopy).
3 Excision of the nodule and bowel resection because of bowel substenosis (laparotomy).
* Significantly different from the other groups.

must be considered as the treatment of choice. Bowel resection is indicated only in cases of rectal bleeding or sigmoidal or rectal stenosis.

Conclusion

Peritoneal endometriosis, the different aspects of which (black, red and white) represent distinctive steps in the evolutionary process, can be explained by the transplantation theory. Red lesions are the most active and most highly vascularized lesions and are considered to be the first stage of peritoneal endometriosis.

The retroperitoneal nodule is an adenomyotic nodule whose histopathogenesis is not related to the implantation of regurgitated endometrial cells but to metaplasia of Müllerian remnants located in the rectovaginal septum. Metaplastic changes of Müllerian rests into adenomyotic glands involving the rectovaginal septum and the retroperitoneal space are responsible for the striking proliferation of the smooth muscle, creating an adenomyomatous appearance similar to that of adenomyosis in the endometrium. In conclusion, *intraperitoneal* and *retroperitoneal* diseases are two different entities with specific histopathogeneses, evolution and symptoms.

References

1 Donnez J, Nisolle M, Casanas-Roux F, Brion P, Da Costa Ferreira N: Stereometric evaluation of peritoneal endometriosis and endometriotic nodules of the rectovaginal septum. Hum Reprod 1996;11:224–228.
2 Donnez J, Nisolle M, Casanas-Roux F, Grandjean P: Endometriosis: Pathogenesis and pathophysiology; in Shaw RW (ed): Endometriosis. Carnforth, Parthenon Publishing, 1990, p 11–19.
3 Halme J, Hammond MG, Hulka JF, Raj SG, Talbert LM: Retrograde menstruation in healthy women and in patients with endometriosis. Obstet Gynecol 1984;64:151–154.
4 Liu DT, Hitchcock A: Endometriosis: its association with retrograde menstruation, dysmenorrhea and tubal pathology. Br J Obstet Gynaecol 1986;93:859–862.
5 Keettel WC, Stein RJ: The viability of the cast-off menstrual endometrium. Am J Obstet Gynecol 1951;61:440–442.
6 Kruitwagen RF, Poels LG, Willemsen WN, de Ronde IJ, Jap PH, Rolland R: Endometrial epithelial cells in peritoneal fluid during the early follicular phase. Fertil Steril 1991;55:297–303.
7 Te Linde RW, Scott RB: Experimental endometriosis. Am J Obstet Gynecol 1950;60:1147–1173.
8 Scott RB, Te Linde RW, Wharton LR Jr: Further studies on experimental endometriosis. Am J Obstet Gynecol 1953;66:1082–1103.
9 Schenken RS, Asch RH, Williams RF, Hodgen GD: Etiology of infertility in monkeys with endometriosis: luteinized unruptured follicles, luteal phase defects, pelvic adhesions, and spontaneous abortions. Fertil Steril 1984;41:122–130.
10 Donnez J, Wayembergh M, Casanas-Roux F, Karaman Y, Willems T, Ferin J: Effect on ovulation of surgically induced endometriosis in rabbits. Gynecol Obstet Invest 1987;24:131–137.

11 Foidart JM, Beliard A, Donnez J: Endometriosis and invasion; in Brosens I, Donnez J (ed): The Current Status of Endometriosis Research and Management. Carnforth, Parthenon Publishing, 1993, pp 35–39.
12 Lessey BA, Damjanovich L, Coutifaris C, Castelbaum A, Albelda SM, Buck CA: Integrin adhesion molecules in the human endometrium. Correlation with the normal and abnormal menstrual cycle. J Clin Invest 1992;90:188–195.
13 Tabibzadeh S, Sun XZ: Cytokine expression in human endometrium throughout the menstrual cycle. Hum Reprod 1992;7:1214–1221.
14 Marbaix E, Kokorine I, Henriet P, Donnez J, Courtoy PJ, Eeckhout Y: The expression of interstitial collagenase in human endometrium is controlled by progesterone and by oestradiol and is related to menstruation. Biochem J 1995;305:1027–1030.
15 Marbaix E, Kokorine I, Donnez J, Eeckhout Y, Courtoy PJ: Regulation and restricted expression of interstitial collagenase suggest a pivotal role in the initiation of menstruation. Hum Reprod 1996;11(suppl 2):134–143.
16 Kokorine I, Marbaix E, Henriet P, Okada Y, Donnez J, Eeckhout Y, Courtoy PJ: Focal cellular origin and regulation of interstitial collagenase (matrix-metalloproteinase-1) are related to menstrual breakdown in the human endometrium. J Cell Sci 1996;109:2151–2160.
17 Kokorine I, Nisolle M, Donnez J, Eeckhout Y, Courtoy PJ, Marbaix E: Expression of interstitial collagenase (matrix metalloproteinase-1) is related to the activity of human endometriotic lesions. Fertil Steril 1997;68:246–251.
18 Spuijbroek MD, Dunselman GA, Menheere PP, Evers JL: Early endometriosis invades the extracellular matrix. Fertil Steril 1992;58:929–933.
19 Gaetje R, Kotzian S, Herrmann G, Baumann R, Starzinski-Powitz A: Invasiveness of endometriotic cells in vitro. Lancet 1995;346:1463–1464.
20 Jenkins S, Olive DL, Haney AF: Endometriosis: pathogenetic implications of the anatomic distribution. Obstet Gynecol 1986;67:335–338.
21 Nisolle M: Peritoneal, ovarian and rectovaginal endometriosis are three distinct entities. Thèse d'Agrégation de l'Enseignement Supérieur, Université Catholique de Louvain, 1996.
22 Nisolle M, Donnez J (eds): Peritoneal, Ovarian and Rectovaginal Endometriosis: The Identification of Three Separate diseases. Carnforth, Parthenon Publishing, 1996.
23 Nisolle M, Casanas-Roux F, Anaf V, Mine JM, Donnez J: Morphometric study of the stromal vascularization in peritoneal endometriosis. Fertil Steril 1993;59:681–684.
24 Donnez J, Nisolle M: L'endométriose péritonéale, le kyste endometriotique ovarien et le nodule de la lame rectovaginale sont trois pathologies différentes (éditorial). Références en Gynécologie Obstétrique 1995;3:121–123.
25 Oosterlynck DJ, Meuleman C, Sobis H, Vandeputte M, Koninckx PR: Angiogenic activity of peritoneal fluid from women with endometriosis. Fertil Steril 1993;59:778–782.
26 Van Langendonckt A, Casanas-Roux F, Donnez J: Oxidative stress and peritoneal endometriosis. Fertil Steril 2002;77:861–870.
27 Halliwell B, Gutteridge JM: Role of free radicals and catalytic metal ions in human disease: an overview. Methods Enzymol 1990;186:1–85.
28 Hippeli S, Elstner EF: Transition metal ion-catalyzed oxygen activation during pathogenic processes. FEBS Lett 1999;443:1–7.
29 Arumugam K, Yip YC: De novo formation of adhesions in endometriosis: the role of iron and free radical reactions. Fertil Steril 1995;64:62–64.
30 Murphy AA, Palinski W, Rankin S, Morales AJ, Parthasarathy S: Macrophage scavenger receptor(s) and oxidatively modified proteins in endometriosis. Fertil Steril 1998;69:1085–1091.
31 Moen MH, Halvorsen TB: Histologic confirmation of endometriosis in different peritoneal lesions. Acta Obstet Gynecol Scand 1992;71:337–342.
32 Stowell SB, Wiley CM, Perez-Reyes N, Powers CN: Cytologic diagnosis of peritoneal fluids. Applicability to the laparoscopic diagnosis of endometriosis. Acta Cytol 1997;41:817–822.
33 Ponka P, Beaumont C, Richardson DR: Function and regulation of transferrin and ferritin. Semin Hematol 1998;35:35–54.
34 Fischbach FA, Gregory DW, Harrison PM, Hoy TG, Williams JM: On the structure of hemosiderin and its relationship to ferritin. J Ultrastruct Res 1971;37:495–503.
35 Casanas-Roux F, Van Langendonckt A, Nisolle M, Donnez J: Iron deposits and oxidative stress in the peritoneal cavity of patients with endometriosis (abstract no 10); in Abstracts of the Endometriosis 7th Biennial World Congress, London, 2000.
36 Murphy AA, Zhou MH, Malkapuram S, Santanam N, Parthasarathy S, Sidell N: RU486-induced growth inhibition of human endometrial cells. Fertil Steril 2000;74:1014–1019.
37 Guérin P, El Mouatassim S, Ménézon Y: Oxidative stress and protection against reactive oxygen species in the pre-implantation embryo and its surroundings. Hum Reprod Update 2001;7:175–189.
38 Sampson JA: Intestinal adenomas of endometrial type. Arch Surg 1922;5:21–27.
39 Donnez J, Nisolle M, Casanas-Roux F, Bassil S, Anaf V: Rectovaginal septum, endometriosis or adenomyosis: Laparoscopic management in a series of 231 patients. Hum Reprod 1995;10:630–635.
40 Donnez J, Nisolle M, Smoes P, Gillet N, Beguin S, Casanas-Roux F: Peritoneal endometriosis and 'endometriotic' nodules of the rectovaginal septum are two different entities. Fertil Steril 1996;66:362–368.
41 Koninckx PR, Martin DC: Deep endometriosis: A consequence of infiltration or retraction or possibly adenomyosis externa? Fertil Steril 1992;58:924–928.
42 Brosens IA: Is mild endometriosis a progressive disease? Hum Reprod 1994;9:2209–2211.
43 Scully RE, Richardson GS, Barlow JF: The development of malignancy in endometriosis. Clin Obstet Gynecol 1966;9:384–411.
44 Reich H, McGlynn F, Salvat J: Laparoscopic treatment of cul-de-sac obliteration secondary to retrocervical deep fibrotic endometriosis. J Reprod Med 1991;36:516–522.
45 Donnez J, Nisolle M, Casanas-Roux F, Anaf V, Smets M: Laparoscopic treatment of rectovaginal septum endometriosis; in Donnez J, Nisolle M (ed): An atlas of laser operative laparoscopy and hysteroscopy. Carnforth, Parthenon Publishing, 1994, pp 75–85.
46 Donnez J, Nisolle M: Advanced laparoscopic sugery for the removal of rectovaginal septum endometriotic and adenomyotic nodules. Baillieres Clin Obstet Gynaecol 1995;9:769–774.
47 Donnez J, Nisolle M, Gillerot S, Smets M, Bassil S, Casanas-Roux F: Rectovaginal septum adenomyotic nodules: A series of 500 cases. Br J Obstet Gynaecol 1997;104:1014–1018.
48 Donnez J, Nisolle M, Squifflet J: Ureteral endometriosis: a complication of rectovaginal endometriotic (adenomyotic) nodules. Fertil Steril 2002;77:32–37.

Post-Presentation Discussion

Professor Taketani: Thank you, Professor Donnez. I now open this paper up for discussion.

Professor Terakawa: Professor Donnez, I am wondering how you can definitively say that all rectovaginal endometriosis are adenomyotic nodules caused by metaplasia of Müllerian remnants, and not from infiltration of peritoneal endometriosis? Dr. Koninckx proposed that there are three types of rectovaginal endometriosis. How can you exclude the possibility of deeply infiltrating rectovaginal endometriosis?

Professor Donnez: I am certain that Philip Koninckx is now changing his mind about this matter. There is a lot of confusion if you look at the literature. Prof. Koninckx has also described what he called a degree 1. This refers to peritoneal endometriosis, and it is uterosacral endometriosis with retraction of the Douglas peritoneum and consequent adhesions to the rectum. At that time, if you look again at the paper of Koninckx et al. in 1992, he was not convinced himself that deeply infiltrating endometriosis could explain the presence of a nodular lesion in the retroperitoneal space (type 3 in the Koninckx classification). He already mentioned the term adenomyosis externa in 1992, and gave this as a possibility. Brosens and I were convinced that this nodular lesion should have a retroperitoneal origin. Koninckx at that time was working with Dan Martin, and for the American researchers, the focus is always on infiltration. But I agree that peritoneal endometriosis could infiltrate the uterosacral ligaments. However, how can you imagine the peritoneum being free of lesions, and to have behind this a lesion of 3 cm in size? I cannot imagine that a small spot of endometriosis of 1 mm can provoke a nodular lesion of 3 cm in size just by infiltration. Why imagine that incidentally one cell goes into the peritoneum because it's situated in the retroperitoneal tissue and creates a lesion like that? This seems illogical to me. Moreover, we cannot recognize genetically the same findings in the retroperitoneal nodule that we have observed in peritoneal endometriosis. I am attempting to use gene analysis to differentiate the origins of female tissue, including fallopian tube, uterus, cervix, endometrium, and vagina, based on their different genetic expression. We are now working on proving that deep adenomyotic nodules have nothing to do with endometrium and with endometriosis.

Dr. Momoeda: I have a question about the rectovaginal adenomyosis etiology. According to my experience, there are many cases involving rectovaginal endometriosis complicated by a peritoneal lesion or endometrial cyst. According to your hypothesis, there is a common background for both etiologies. Would you comment on that?

Professor Donnez: One of the first arguments I have in favor of the retroperitoneal origin is that in 28% of cases of a nodule, there is no peritoneal lesion. But this means that in 72% of cases there is mixed endometriosis, peritoneal endometriosis, ovarian endometriosis, and rectovaginal nodules. I believe that Prof. Fujii from Japan in the past was in favor of the metaplasia theory. It could be that many things could be explained by metaplasia, even if we accept the concept of reflux. However, the 7% of women who have a complex peritoneal ovarian rectovaginal lesion probably have a genetic sensitivity to develop this type of pathology. I really hope that, in the future, genetic analysis using microarrays will help us identify a subgroup of patients who are very sensitive to developing this type of pathology. It is the same as for diethylstilbestrol-induced disease. How many thousands of young female fetuses have been influenced by diethylstilbestrol taken by their mother? And yet only 1–3% of women have developed vaginal adenomyosis. It is much more common for women to develop uterine anomalies, characterized by the typical T-shaped uterus. Thus, there is surely sensitivity among a certain type of patient, and it is important for the prevention of endometriosis in the near future to identify this group of women. I'm sure that there is a common background, but I cannot determine what it is at the present time. There are different entities and each must be treated according to the symptomatology and according to the site of lesions.

Dr. Suginami: When we examine the pelvis of women, we sometimes encounter cases of Masters and Allen syndrome, which is a pocket formation. And at the bottom of the pocket, we sometimes find endometriosis present. Isn't it possible to argue in this sense that rectovaginal endometriosis can or may develop from this endometriosis?

Professor Donnez: Rectovaginal nodules, which have an origin between the uterosacral ligaments, often have a median localization. The pockets are often situated outside the uterosacral ligaments. I agree that very often you will observe by laparoscopy some endometriotic lesions in cases of Masters and Allen syndrome, if you look very closely in the peritoneal pocket. But all of these lesions are very superficial. I have never seen one case of a nodule in one pocket. Thus, I agree with your hypothesis in general, but I don't think it's realistic in practice. Because if you have a case of a nodule originating from a peritoneal defect, please let me know about it. I would be very interested in such a finding, as I am still researching the histogenesis of that.

Dr. Obata: We observed ovarian endometriosis around ovarian cancer, especially clear cell adenocarcinoma and endometrial carcinoma. This was not endometriomas. I would guess that the histogenesis is different between endometriomas and other ovarian endometriosis. Could you comment on the histogenesis of other types of ovarian endometriosis?

Professor Donnez: In San Diego, I saw a poster, perhaps from Japan, describing a relationship between ovarian endometriomas and ovarian adenocarcinoma. I was very surprised to read that, because among the approximately 20,000 cases of endometriosis treated in my department over the last 25 years, we have had only one case in a woman of 48 years with an ovarian endometrioma that was suspected on vaginal echography because of the presence of intrapapillary vegetations and intracystic septa, where we were able to see a continuum between ovarian endometrial tissue and the adenocarcinoma. I think that this type of case is very, very infrequent. I agree that it could also be from another origin. We have no explanation, but the association, at least in my country, between ovarian endometriomas and ovarian adenocarcinoma is extremely rare. I agree that it could also be due to a genetic difference. In both Japan and Belgium, there are a lot of women with endometriosis and its prevalence is dramatically and significantly increasing. Thus, there is surely a genetic basis, but so far we are unable to explain it. It could be that some environmental toxins induce some gene expression and then favor the appearance of endometriosis.

Professor Taketani: Dr. Donnez, I would like to discuss the natural history of endometriosis. Everybody agrees that endometriosis is a self-limiting disease. And as you mentioned, the sequence of progression of endometriotic foci is as follows; first, there is a red lesion, second, there is a black lesion, and finally, a white lesion. White lesions seem to represent a very dormant and quiescent stage. In fact, the natural course of endometriosis differs from patient to patient. Furthermore, if we look at an individual case, the fate of endometriotic foci in the peritoneum also differs among the foci. Thus, I would like to know what determines the fate of each endometriotic focus. This knowledge will be very advantageous, and will influence strategies in the treatment of endometriosis. Do you have any comment on this?

Professor Donnez: I fully agree with this concept of natural evolution of the disease. My impression is that endometriosis is becoming more and more prevalent among younger women, starting as early as 14 and 15 years of age. I have the impression that after 40 years of age, the activity of the disease decreases, and I would suggest that there is a peak of activity between 25 and 35. What about this de-evolution from red, black, and white lesions? I think that this is the natural history in some patients. I agree with you that in some patients the natural course is from red lesions, to black, and finally to white lesions. However, in another group of patients, the disease will continue, and the patient will develop more and more red and black lesions in a repetitive manner. We don't know why the natural history will be one way for one patient, and another way for another patient. Thus, I am in complete disagreement with the expectant management approach. I think that it is unethical to do a diagnostic laparoscopy followed by expectant management. If you see lesions, you have to destroy them, because no one can say for certain that, for example, a black lesion is quiescent and thus will have no influence. We cannot conclude definitively that a given lesion will not be able to regrow from another factor that we cannot determine now. It is for this reason that we need to continue to hold this type of conference in the future. There remains a lot that we need to know about this disease.

Dr. Suginami: I sometimes find clear vesicles among a younger generation of patients, those that are 12, 13, 14, and maybe up to 15 years of age. If I biopsy them, I will surely find endometriosis in the clear vesicles, with no vascularization, and no bleeding whatsoever, just clear papules. Can you comment on your experience?

Professor Donnez: If you look at the book I have written on this subject, you will see that I consider clear vesicles to be very active lesions. I place them in the same group as red lesions. The clear vesicle is a glandular excrescence, and it is probably at the phase of attachment. If you ask your pathologist to give you more information about the biopsy, he will tell you that the ectopic endometrium taken from a clear vesicle is identical to the eutopic endometrium. It is very fresh, and the clear vesicle is likely the first step of attachment before the lesion has induced neovascularization and proliferation in the retroperitoneal space. I think that clear vesicles represent just the phase of attachment to the peritoneum. Something that you mentioned yourself provides a clue about their nature. You said that they occur in young girls, aged 13 and 14 years. This means that this is the first stage of the disease.

Dr. Suginami: I completely agree with you.

Professor Donnez: It's important to treat these young women by medical therapy after laparoscopic destruction by stopping the menstrual reflux, because if you fail to do so, by the time this individual reaches an age when she wants to become pregnant, perhaps 10 years later, she will likely be in stage 4 endometriosis.

Professor Hoshiai: I have just two questions. The first question is about deep endometriosis. Do you have any experience with deep endometriosis associated with adenomyosis?

Professor Donnez: With uterine adenomyosis?

Professor Hoshiai: Yes. My question is whether adenomyosis originates as an invasion of the retroperitoneal space. I am not sure, with regard to the pathogenesis of adenomyosis, whether the endometrium is able to infuse the retroperitoneal space. I am sure that it cannot invade the myometrium, or smooth muscle layer.

Professor Donnez: No, 99% of the patients with rectovaginal adenomyosis have no uterine adenomyosis. In the past, I was convinced that the origin was the rectovaginal septum. More and more, I am convinced that the origin is the area of attachment of the vaginal mucosa to the posterior part of the cervix. And now with MRI, which we can do systematically, we are increasingly convinced that it should be considered, for example, as an extension of retrocervical adenomyosis. This is certainly where it originates. It has nothing to do with uterine adenomyosis, but we have to determine why incidentally over the past 10 years adenomyosis has been shown to develop in the retroperitoneal space. To date, I have no explanation for this. When you do a serial section of such a nodule, you can sometimes cut 1 cm of the nodule without observing endometrial tissue. Only smooth muscle hyperplasia is visible. This smooth muscle hyperplasia invading the nerves produces pelvic pain.

Professor Hoshiai: My other question is about peritoneal lesions. You said that retrograde menstruation occurs, and that attachment is the first step, but we can find endometrium in the peritoneal cavity. I think almost all women experience this. Moreover, matrix metalloproteinase is also very common. However, I would like to ask you about heme oxygenase 1 and 2, which may act as promoters of implantation of endometria to the peritoneum. At present, you describe heme oxygenase as the most important of such promoters.

Professor Donnez: No, I think it is just one of the factors. I think that many enzymes are involved in the pathogenesis of endometriosis. My first hypothesis when I began doing this research was that women with endometriosis did not have enough heme oxygenases. It turns out they have active heme oxygenases, and thus it is not a defect in enzyme production, but it could be that the system of degradation of heme is overwhelmed in the endometriotic patient. This patient would develop endometriosis because she was unable to destroy all the endometrial debris present in the peritoneal cavity. I agree that many other factors are responsible. The problem is that we don't know whether the presence of the macrophage is the consequence or the origin of the endometriosis. That is one of the major complications for all fields of research.

Professor Hoshiai: How old was the youngest patient with endometriosis in your experience?

Professor Donnez: In my experience, it was a patient who had only experienced menstrual bleeding seven times. She was really the youngest; she was 12 years old.

Professor Terakawa: I would like to return to the discussion of malignant transformation of ovarian endometriomas. The incidence as reported in a Western textbook is 0.7%, and the same frequency has been reported recently in Japan. You give a different incidence in your lecture and in your experience. Could you comment on that?

Professor Donnez: What was the age of the patients in that group?

Professor Terakawa: Overall.

Professor Donnez: I think that the first distinction we have to make is the age of the patient. As I mentioned this morning, I have never seen a patient with malignant transformation of an ovarian endometrioma who was less than 40 years old. Around menopause, the situation is completely different. My department is similar to other departments worldwide, in that we have many cases of ovarian endometrioid adenocarcinoma. However, it is not called 'endometrioid' because it is a consequence of malignant transformation of endometriosis. It is called 'endometrioid' because some aspects are similar to endometrial carcinoma. It is not a sufficient argument to say that ovarian endometrioid adenocarcinoma is due to the malignant transformation of ovarian endometriomas. If this were the case, we would have to establish in serial sections a histological continuum between normal endometriosis and adenocarcinoma. In nearly all cases of ovarian endometrioid adenocarcinoma in my department, the pathologist was unable to do so. Thus, I am not sure that the incidence is so high. Nonetheless, I would agree that if a patient more than 45 years of age presents to my department with a suspected endometrioma (intracystic papillary lesions), we will propose bilateral adnexectomy, because you can never be sure that in a certain part there is adenocarcinoma. To date, we have done that systematically and we have never observed, for example, adenocarcinoma in situ, arising from an endometrial cyst.

What we can observe very readily in ovarian endometrioma is the presence of atypical cells, and some gynecologists will conclude that there could be a risk of adenocarcinoma, and they would argue for cystectomy instead of vaporization of the internal cyst wall. In the paper on ovarian endometriomas I published 15 years ago, I mentioned that areas of atypical hyperplasia were present in 20% of cases of ovarian endometriomas. But it was considered to be an inflammatory reaction. If you look in the literature, 20 years before my paper, Czernobilsky described the presence of atypical cells in ovarian endometriomas, and had already suggested that it was the consequence of inflammation in the tissue.

Gynecologic and
Obstetric Investigation

Gynecol Obstet Invest 2002;54(suppl 1):63–64
DOI: 10.1159/000066287

Summary

Yuji Taketani, Tokyo University

Fortunately for the many women who suffer from endometriosis, new research supports the development of more effective management for this chronic disorder. This supplement featured many interesting and informative presentations and discussions that were heard at the Takeda-sponsored 5th Japan Conference on Endometriosis held on May 18, 2002, in Hakone, Japan. Promising areas of research include combined medical and surgical treatment, optimal positioning for uterosacral nerve ablation, and pretreatment of ovarian endometrial cysts before in-vitro fertilization.

Because neither medical therapy nor surgical therapy alone have been completely satisfactory for treatment of endometriosis-associated infertility and pelvic pain, Professor Jacques Donnez (Universite Catholique de Louvain) reviewed the literature to determine whether combining the two methods would provide effective symptomatic relief. He reported average pregnancy rates of 42% and 50% after combined medical-laparoscopic treatment. Although Professor Donnez cautioned that it may be difficult to reach a consensus, available data strongly support the view that visible endometriosis should be removed, and that GnRH agonists are effective prior to such surgery for moderate and severe endometriosis.

In his second presentation, Professor Donnez summarized current thinking on the histogenesis of peritoneal, ovarian, and rectovaginal endometriosis. He reported that the three different peritoneal lesions, red, black, and white, represent distinct steps in an evolutionary process that is explained by the transplantation theory. Professor Donnez believes that ovarian lesions most likely develop from metaplastic transformation of invaginated epithelial inclusion cysts from the ovarian epithelial layer, which is originally derived from celomic epithelium. Rectovaginal endometriotic lesions are derived from metaplastic conversion of Müllerian rests into endometriotic glands in the rectovaginal septum. This supplement also includes an article by Professor Donnez's colleague, Dr. Jean Squifflet, on the diagnosis and imaging of adenomyotic disease of the retroperitoneal space.

Dr. Miho Fujii (Sapporo Medical University) used antibodies for specific nerve systems to discover that parasympathetic nerves predominate in the uterosacral ligament, and that sensory nerves comprise only 20% of all nerves in the area. Dr. Fujii showed that the area 2 cm distal to the uterine cervix was the optimal site for uterosacral nerve ablation and that 1.5 cm was the recommended depth for relief of the pain associated with functional dysmenorrhea. This study will be of great help in conducting LUNA or in managing the patient with painful endometriosis, and has also served to clarify the link between endometriosis and pain.

Dr. Mikio Momoeda (University of Tokyo) studied survey results of 1,092 women with confirmed endometriosis to discover that chronic pelvic pain and dyspareunia increased with disease progression. This association persisted regardless of whether the women's chief complaint was pain or infertility. However, because dysmenorrhea was related to disease severity only in the subgroup of infertile women, Dr. Momoeda concluded that dysmenorrhea may be caused by a variety of mechanisms unrelated to endometriosis in women with pain as their chief complaint.

KARGER

Fax + 41 61 306 12 34
E-Mail karger@karger.ch
www.karger.com

0378–7346/02/0545–0063$18.50/0

Accessible online at:
www.karger.com/goi

According to Dr. Souichi Yoshida (Tottori University), laparoscopic surgery is an effective treatment for pain relief and restoration of fertility in women with ovarian endometrioma. Dr. Yoshida reported that serum levels of interleukin 6 are significantly higher in those with this common lesion and concluded that serum IL-6 will have important clinical relevance to the management of endometriosis

By reviewing diagnostic and surgical laparoscopic records from 732 infertile women, Dr. Naoyuki Takuma (Asahikawa Medical College) reported that the overall pregnancy rate after diagnostic laparotomy was 40%. Pregnancy rates after surgical laparotomy were 37.9% for complete or incomplete removal; about 50% after incomplete removal; 26.1% after ethanol fixation of the endometrioma, and 70% after ethanol fixation followed by assisted reproductive technology. Dr. Takuma cautions that complete removal of the cyst may damage the ovary.

By analyzing the outcomes of women undergoing in-vitro fertilization with or without cystectomy or aspiration of the ovarian cyst, Dr. Nobuhiko Suganuma (Toyohashi Municipal Hospital) has shown that, although treatment of cysts reduced the number of retrieved oocytes and oocyte quality was not affected by the presence of a cyst, aspiration of the cyst did improve the rate of fertilization. Dr. Suganuma concluded that diagnostic laparoscopic techniques for infertile women could be improved.

Although there is much left to learn about endometriosis, progress has been made in the management of this common disorder. The pain and infertility associated with endometriosis are slowly yielding to new treatments and techniques available to the modern physician. We hope the information presented in this supplement will inspire and motivate physicians to understand and manage the enigmatic disease that is endometriosis.